HELP, I HAVE TO TEACH ROCK AND MINERAL IDENTIFICATION AND I'M NOT A GEOLOGIST!

THE DEFINITIVE GUIDE FOR TEACHERS AND HOME SCHOOL PARENTS FOR TEACHING ROCK AND MINERAL IDENTIFICATION TO ELEMENTARY, MIDDLE AND HIGH SCHOOL STUDENTS

Tracy DJ Barnhart

Tracy Barnhart / Giverny Press
1121 Park West Blvd, Suite B#159
Mt. Pleasant, SC 29466
www.TracyBarnhart.com
www.MiniMeGeology.com

While the author has made every effort to provide accurate Internet addresses at the time of publication, neither the publisher nor the author assumes any responsibility for errors, or for changes that occur after publication. Further, the author and publisher do not have control over and do not assume any responsibility for third party websites or their content.

Help, I Have to Teach Rock and Mineral Identification and I'm Not a Geologist! / Tracy DJ Barnhart. —1st ed..

ISBN 978-0-9894112-2-6

Library of Congress Control Number: 2017911289

Printed in the United States of America

Contents

INTRODUCTION

Welcome to *Help, I Have to Teach Rock and Mineral Identification and I'm Not a Geologist!* I hope you find this book fun and informative. Not everyone who teaches rock and mineral identification is a geologist by trade, but that should not stop you from instilling a sense of wonder in your students about our Earth. This book will help you do just that.

I designed this book to give you the tools to explain rock and mineral identification to elementary, middle and high school students. The information in this book will allow you to customize your lessons and activities for different ages. This book is not based on any particular set of rocks or minerals so you can adapt the lessons to the samples you have on hand. If you need samples, I can help you choose the best set or loose samples for your activities.

If you have any questions about teaching rock and mineral identification, please contact me directly! My email is tracyb@minimegeology.com.

Sincerely,
Tracy Barnhart, Owner
Giverny, Inc. / Mini Me Geology

CHAPTER 1

ROCK AND MINERAL IDENTIFICATION BASICS

Children love rocks and minerals. They are the building blocks of our Earth and are fascinating to study and collect. There are hundreds of rocks and minerals in the world, giving students opportunities to study numerous varieties of samples. Geologists use a variety of tests and information to determine the name of a rock or mineral. Students can perform most of the tests in a classroom or at home, making science lessons fun and educational!

1.1   Tips for Teaching Rock and Mineral Identification

Identifying rock and mineral samples can seem daunting to students. Elementary students are experiencing rocks and minerals for the first time while middle and high schools students may have only limited knowledge from earlier grades. Teaching children the basic properties that distinguish minerals and rocks from one another can help students begin to understand the basic fundamentals of geology. Younger students may use simple sets of rocks and minerals to gain an understanding of the differences while middle and high school students can learn to identify multiple samples within a particular group, such as minerals, igneous rocks, metamorphic rocks and sedimentary rocks, or between groups at a more advanced level.

**Tip #1:** Use a hands-on learning method where you give the students physical samples they can touch and test. A picture or poster is not as effective at teaching as hands-on learning. Allow the children to test the samples without worrying about damaging the minerals or rocks. Some of the tests they will perform will scratch, rub or even break the samples but that is okay and is part of learning to identify the properties. In addition, make sure that the samples are pure or almost pure specimens so that the tests are accurate and do not confuse students with the presence of two or more rock or mineral types. If two or more mineral or rock types are present, the test results may be incorrect.

**Tip #2:** Supply the students with high quality, proper tools to use in the identification process. Black and white streak plates, hand lenses, pennies older than 1982, strong vinegar and metal paper clips are all useful for identification purposes. Ensure that younger students have proper supervision using household acids. The next section discusses details of some of the geologist's tools that may be useful for your lessons.

**Tip #3:** Use flow charts that are easy to read with limited arrow options so the choices are obvious for very young students. Older students may use information sheets, posters and flow charts that have additional data about the most important properties of the rocks and minerals. Flow charts are helpful because they give students a specific pattern to follow when performing tests and eliminating possibilities as you move from one block to another across the chart. Older children often find information cards or sheets helpful because they can perform the tests in any manner they choose and use the process of elimination to determine the identity of an unknown mineral. For students who are very interested in additional information about the minerals they identify, a copy of a rock and mineral reference book might be fun for them to review. Mini Me Geology has a list of six fabulous rock and mineral information books on our blog that we recommend for students of varying ages and interests.

Tip #4: Limit sample sets for younger children to two to three rocks or minerals that have significantly different properties. For older children who easily master the two to three sample sets, you can give them larger sample sets to try to identify. Some suggested sample sets are provided in each section.

Tip #5: Allow children to work on their own before walking them through the solution. Identifying rock and mineral samples will help students develop logical thinking skills that transfer from science to other subjects. When you give the samples to the children, explain the properties that they will use to identify their samples and show them how to walk through the flow chart or identification sheets to find the answers. Take your time with the exercises. The more you practice the better you become at sample identification.

1.2   *How to Perform an Experiment*

The process of identifying rocks and minerals includes a lot of testing and experimenting to determine the properties of each sample. Geologists use experiments to learn new things about their samples. Experiments are like recipes, you follow a certain set of steps to perform your experiment and to observe the results. Geologists often use a notebook to record the steps of their experiments. Have students write the information for each test on a piece of paper or in a science notebook. Students can perform and record each of the following steps during their experiments. While this may seem like too much work for a single test, you can also use it to identify a single sample, performing multiple identification tests within Step 3.

Step 1: State the Question

The first step of any experiment is to know what you are trying to learn. Are you trying to learn the streak of a certain mineral? Are you trying to learn if a sample will sink or float? Are you trying to observe the texture of a rock? Are you trying to determine the name of the mineral? When you start your experiment, have students write down the question that they are trying to answer.

Step 2: Form Your Hypothesis

The next step in any experiment is to try to guess the results. This is called your "hypothesis." Remember, the hypothesis is just a guess and you may or may not be right. If it turns out that the student's hypothesis is incorrect, ensure that they know it is okay and part of the process of performing the experiment. The point of an experiment is to find the answer regardless of whether their initial guess was correct or incorrect. Testing the hypothesis is the point of the experiment. Remember to have students write the hypothesis on their paper or in a science notebook.

Step 3: Perform the Test(s)

The third step is to perform the test(s). Have students follow the steps of the experiment closely so you know that the result is correct. For rock and mineral identification, the steps of the experiment could be as simple as rubbing the sample on a streak plate or placing it in a glass of water. Regardless of the simplicity of the test, make sure students perform the test correctly and accurately. If you are using the overall experiment to determine the name of a rock or mineral, use this step to perform all of the identification tests.

Step 4: Observe and Evaluate the Results

After students perform the test(s), ask them to observe and evaluate the results. What happened? Was their hypothesis correct? If not, why was the result different than what they expected?

Step 5: Record the Results

Ask students to record the observations on their paper or in a science notebook. Students can record notes, photos, drawings and their thoughts about the results. They can even write down if they liked the experiment or if they would like to do the experiment again with a different rock or mineral. There is never too many data when recording thoughts and observation of an experiment. Learning to take detailed notes will also help students to develop good note-taking skills for future classes and tests.

1.3   Tools of the Geologist

What is a Geologist? A Geologist is a person who studies the Earth. Geologists use different tools and instruments to perform their work. When identifying rocks and minerals, geologists use tools ranging from basic to complex. For students, there are a few simple tools that they can use to help them figure out the name of a mineral or rock. Some are even household items.

Hand Lens

Hand lenses are hand-held magnifiers. Some hand lenses have one magnification while others have multiple. For example, a Mini Me Geology hand lens has two different strengths – 3X and 6X. The large area has a 3X magnification, which means that the object you are looking at will appear to be three times bigger than its normal size. The smaller area has a 6X magnification, which means that the object you are looking at will appear to be six times bigger than its normal size.

To use a hand lens, start by choosing a rock or mineral sample to examine. Hold the mineral on the opposite side of the hand lens from your eye. If you have two magnifications, start by looking through the larger area of the hand magnifier, 3X in the case of a Mini Me Geology lens. You can move the mineral or the hand lens until you can see clearly through the lens. If you want to see certain parts of the sample more closely, use the smaller 6X area and focus the lens using the same method.

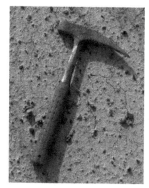

Rock Hammer

Geologists use special hammers to break rocks and minerals. A rock hammer has a flat end and a pointed end. You can use each end of the hammer to break rock and mineral samples to study fresh surfaces and to investigate the shape a mineral will form when it breaks.

Safety Goggles

Geologists use safety goggles (also called safety glasses) to protect their eyes from sharp rock and mineral chips and other materials when studying and performing experiments with rocks and minerals. Always be safe and wear safety goggles when experimenting with rocks and minerals.

Field Notebook

Geologists use field notebooks to record their findings when they are outside mapping rocks and minerals or in the office studying and experimenting with their samples. Geologists write notes about their studies and draw pictures and maps of their rocks and minerals in the notebook. Some field notebooks even have waterproof paper so that the geologist's work will not be lost if they get caught in the rain!

Streak Plates

Streak plates are useful tools to help you determine the identity of a mineral. Streak plates are pieces of unglazed porcelain tile that come in white and black and different sizes. When geologists use streak plates, they are creating a mineral powder that may or may not be the same color as the mineral.

Over time, streak plates become dirty. You can clean them by using a warm soapy water mixture and a kitchen sponge or Magic Eraser.

Penny (pre-1982)

Pennies that pre-date 1982 are useful for determining mineral hardness because they have a specific number on the Mohs hardness scale. Due to the change in the metal content in 1982, newer pennies do not have the same hardness as older pennies, making them unreliable for hardness testing. Students can try to scratch a mineral with the penny during hardness testing.

Lemon Juice or Vinegar

Lemon juice and vinegar are weak acids that students can use to determine the presence or absence of calcite in a rock or mineral sample. Calcite "fizzes" in the presence of acid. Geologists often use a weak hydrochloric acid for the tests because the reaction is stronger and easier to see. Older students can use hydrochloric acid under adult supervision. When students use lemon juice or vinegar, it is helpful to use a hand lens to aid observation of the fizz or bubbles on the rock or mineral's surface.

Glass Plate or Pocket Knife

Glass plates (similar to streak plates) and pocket knives have a similar hardness and are useful to determine the hardness of a mineral. Students can scratch the mineral on a glass plate or use a pocket knife to scratch a mineral for the hardness test.

Steel Paper Clips

Steel paper clips, without the plastic coating, are another household item geologists use to determine the hardness of a mineral. Students can scratch the mineral with a steel paperclip for the hardness test.

Steel File

Steel nail files are another useful household tool for determining the hardness of a mineral. The files are stronger than the other household items mentioned and can help identify some of the hardest minerals in your sample sets. Students can scratch the mineral on a steel file during the hardness test.

Fingernail

Believe it or not, the fingernail is another geologist's tool. Fingernails are on the lower spectrum of the hardness scale and can scratch some of the softest minerals on Earth.

CHAPTER 2

MINERAL IDENTIFICATION

Minerals are all around you! They make up the rocks in the Earth and have many uses, too. A mineral is a naturally occurring, inorganic, homogeneous substance that has a definite chemical composition and crystal structure. Scientists identified over 4,000 minerals on our Earth so far. The minerals vary in chemical composition, ranging from a single element, such as gold or iron, to complex compositions as found in other minerals, such as micas and feldspars. Minerals form in a variety of manners like cooling volcanic magma, precipitation from mineral-rich water and solid state changes from extreme heat and pressure. Silicate minerals are the most common group of minerals found on earth. A mineral group is a family of minerals having a similar chemical composition. Other groups of minerals include carbonates, halides, sulfates, sulfides and oxides. Scientists can also classify groups of minerals based on their crystal structure or lack of structure.

Minerals come in many colors and shapes. Some minerals look very different from each other and some look very similar. Each mineral has a unique set of physical properties that geologists use to tell the minerals apart. The most common physical properties that geologists use to identify minerals are crystal shape, color, luster, streak, hardness, cleavage, fracture, magnetism and optical properties.

2.1   Crystal Shapes

There are many different crystal shapes in the world. In fact, there are too many to list here! Some of the most common minerals and their shapes are listed in the table below. The most interesting part about crystal shapes is that minerals can sometimes form more than one shape depending on how it forms or its environment.

Shape	CUBE	OCTAHEDRON	RHOMBODEDRON	SIX-SIDED PRISM CENTER WITH SIX-SIDED PYRAMIDS ON BOTH ENDS	SIX-SIDED PLATY
Minerals that can form this shape	Halite, Pyrite	Fluorite, Diamond	Calcite, Rhodochrosite	Quartz, Amethyst	Lepidolite Mica

6

Sometimes you will see a mineral that looks like two crystals which have grown together. This is called a "twinned" crystal. Staurolite is a commonly twinned mineral.

Minerals can also form in groups or layers and are attached to one another side by side. This is called a mineral "cluster" or "druze." Quartz, amethyst and citrine are commonly found in a druze form inside geodes.

2.2   Color

Minerals come in many colors. Some minerals only form in one color, like yellow in sulfur, while others can form many different colors, like fluorite, which can be purple, blue, yellow, white, red and green. The color of a mineral depends on the elements that are present in the crystal structure.

2.3   Luster

Luster is the appearance of a mineral when the light shines on the sample. Some are shiny and some are not, but it is important for children to understand that every mineral has a luster. Minerals can have many different lusters, which is why it is another clue to a mineral's identity. There are numerous mineral lusters. Some of the most common that students should understand are:

Glassy: A mineral with a glassy luster shines and reflects light just like real glass. Examples of minerals with a glassy luster include quartz, rhodonite, tourmaline, and epidote. Glassy is the most common luster of all minerals.

Pearly: A pearly luster was actually named from the appearance of an real pearl. Examples of minerals with a pearly luster include talc, lepidolite, and gypsum.

Earthy: A mineral with an earthy luster is not shiny and does not reflect light. The minerals appear dull, like soil. Examples of minerals with a earthy luster include limonite and azurite.

Metallic: A mineral with a metallic luster looks like metal (think quarter, pennies, aluminum foil). Examples of minerals with a metallic luster include pyrite, graphite, and magnetite.

Silky: A mineral with a silky luster looks like it was made of fine silk material. The minerals are often made of many small, thin fibers. Examples of minerals with a silky luster include malachite and ulexite.

Greasy: A mineral with a greasy luster looks as though it were covered with grease. Examples of minerals with a greasy luster include sulfur, halite, and sodalite.

Waxy: a mineral with a waxy luster looks as though it were covered with wax. Examples of minerals with a waxy luster include turquoise and agate.

2.4   *Streak*

The streak is the color of the mineral in powdered form. Testing the streak color is easy and fun and can be a great clue when looking for a mineral's identity. Geologists use streak plates to test a mineral. A streak plate is an unglazed piece of porcelain tile that can be either black or white.

To test a mineral, have the children choose a dark streak plate for light colored minerals and a white streak plate for dark colored minerals. Place the plate on a hard surface and scratch the mineral across the plate. The purpose of the test is to break down some of the mineral into a powder on the plate. If you perform the test correctly, you will wear down part of the mineral sample to make sure children understand that is okay and expected.

A streak plate has a hardness of about 7 on the Mohs Hardness scale, which is similar to quartz and amethyst. So, minerals with a hardness value similar to and above 7, like corundum and diamond, will not show a streak on the plate and will actually scratch the porcelain. For minerals that are similar in hardness to the streak plates, children must press the mineral very hard onto the plate to see the color and may need an adult's help. The harder the mineral, the harder you will likely have to scratch to see the streak.

One reason that streak can be helpful in determining a mineral's identity is that some minerals will streak the same color as their outward color, some will have no streak, and others will have a streak color that is completely different than their outward color. The following tables provide some common examples of minerals and their streak color.

Use white streak plates to test dark colored minerals.

Use black streak plates to test light colored minerals.

	NAME	MINERAL COLOR	STREAK COLOR
Some minerals have the **same streak color** as their sample color.	Azurite	Blue	Blue
	Graphite	Black	Black to Dark Grey
	Limonite	Brown & Yellow	Yellowish-Brown
	Halite	Colorless to White	White

	NAME	MINERAL COLOR	STREAK COLOR
Some minerals have no streak and may stratch the streak plate.	Diamond	Colorless	Will scratch plate
	Ruby	Red	Will scratch plate

	NAME	MINERAL COLOR	STREAK COLOR
Some minerals have a **different streak color** than their sample color.	Sulfur	Yellow	White
	Pyrite	Brassy Yellow "fools gold"	Greenish-Black
	Hematite	Gray	Red to Reddish-Brown
	Amethyst	Purple	White

2.5   *Mineral Density*

Mineral density is the mass of the mineral per unit volume. A common unit of mineral density is grams per cubic centimeter (g/cm^3). In general, geologists can make a few generic observations about mineral density, such as dark colored minerals tend to be denser than light colored minerals, and minerals containing heavy metals tend to be very dense.

In a classroom, students can measure the density of a mineral using a few simple steps. The density of a mineral is calculated by dividing the mass of the mineral by its volume.

Density = Mass / Volume

To calculate the density of a specific mineral sample, first, weigh the sample to determine its mass in grams. Second, use a graduated cylinder and water to determine the volume. Students should fill a graduated cylinder with water until it is approximately half full and then record the exact water level. Next, have students place the mineral sample into the graduated cylinder and measure the water level. The volume of the mineral sample is equal to the initial water level subtracted from the final water level.

Volume of Mineral Sample = Final Water Level – Initial Water Level

The following is an example calculation of a mystery mineral sample:

- Mass of sample measured at 25 g
- Initial water level in cylinder measured at 20 cm^3
- Final water level in cylinder measured at 40 cm^3

Density = Mass / (initial water level – final water level)

$$\text{Density} = \frac{25\ g}{(40cm3 - 20\ cm3)}$$

$$\text{Density} = \frac{25\ g}{(20\ cm3)}$$

$$\text{Density} = 1.25\ \text{g/cm}^3$$

2.6 Hardness

Hardness	Mineral	Household Item
1	Talc	
2	Gypsum	
2.5		Fingernail
3	Calcite	
3.5		Copper Penny (pre-1982)
4	Fluorite	
4.5		Paper Clip
5	Apatite	
5.5		Glass / Pocket Knife
6	Orthoclase Feldspar	
6.5		Steel File
7	Quartz	
8	Topaz	
9	Corundum	
10	Diamond	

Geologists use the hardness of a mineral to help determine the identity of a sample. German geologist, Friedrich Mohs, developed the Mohs Scale of Hardness in 1812. The Mohs scale is a relative scale that lists the hardness of 10 common minerals. Talc, #1 on the scale, is the softest, and diamond, #10, is the hardest. Other common household items are also assigned to the hardness scale, such as glass, fingernail and a pre-1982 penny. The Mohs Scale of Hardness and common objects are listed in the table.

To test the hardness of a mineral, have students try to scratch the surface of an unknown sample with a mineral or object on the hardness scale. If the unknown sample is not scratched by the known mineral or object, the hardness of the unknown sample is greater. For example, if the sample was not scratched by fluorite, the hardness of the unknown sample is greater than 4. If the sample was scratched by apatite then you know the hardness of the sample is less than 5. Therefore, the actual hardness of the unknown sample would be between 4 and 5.

MOHS' HARDNESS SCALE TRIVIA	The first nine minerals on the Mohs' Hardness Scale have nearly the same relative hardness between them. For example, fluorite is four time harder than talc, quartz is severn times harder than talc and corundum is nine times harder than talc. However, the tenth mineral on the scale, diamond, is 40 times harder than talc.

2.7   *Cleavage and Fracture*

Often when you hear geologists talk about minerals you will hear them use the terms "cleavage" and "fracture." Cleavage and fracture properties can provide great clues to a mineral's identity.

<u>*Cleavage*</u>

Minerals with cleavage will break into particular shapes when the crystal is broken, such as cubes, rhombs, octahedrons and thin layers. Some minerals have "perfect cleavage," which means the mineral breaks smoothly along the cleavage plane without any rough edges. The following table provides examples of cleavage types and minerals that exhibit that cleavage.

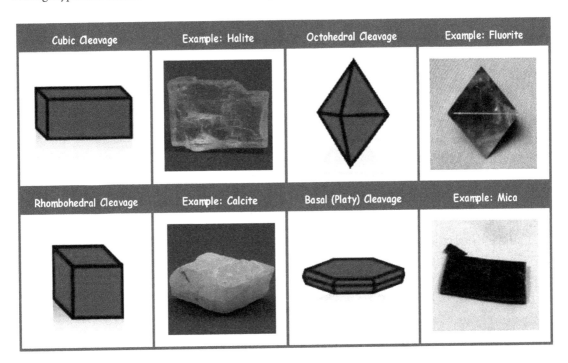

Fracture

Minerals that do not have good cleavage (do not break into specific shapes) will fracture when broken. Even minerals that naturally grow in perfect shapes, such as cubes or prisms, may fracture when they are broken and will no longer be a cube or prism. Two minerals that can have beautiful crystal forms but fracture when they break are quartz and pyrite.

A common fracture pattern is a conchoidal fracture. Minerals and rocks with a conchoidal fracture will have a swirl pattern on the surface after it breaks. Students should use safety goggles and a rock hammer when breaking samples to examine the cleavage or fracture.

2.8   Magnetism

Magnetite's unique property is that it is magnetic. To test a mineral sample to see if it has magnetic properties, you need a metal paper clip that does not have a plastic coating. Have the students lay the paper clip on a table. Slowly touch the sample to the paper clip and see if you can lift it off of the table. Attracting the paperclip may take several tries but be patient and it will work if it has magnetic properties.

2.9   Optical Properties

Iceland Spar Calcite

Some minerals have optical properties, which make them unique. Iceland Spar Calcite is special because it can make images look doubled when you look through the crystal. This property is known as *double refraction*. This type of calcite is a clear sample and due to the rhombohedral shape, text and images appear to be doubled when you place a sample on top as shown in the picture on the left.

Ulexite, also known as "TV Rock," appears to project images from beneath the crystal to the top of the crystal. Ulexite is a fibrous mineral and the structure of the crystal causes the projection of the images.

Ulexite Mineral

2.10   *Calcite Fizz Test*

The calcite mineral is made of calcium carbonate, which reacts with acid. The reaction that you see is the production of bubbles on the surface of the sample. The bubbles are a release of carbon dioxide gas. Geologists use a test, often called the *Fizz Test*, to test rocks for the presence of calcium carbonate. However, you can also use this test on mineral samples.

To perform the test you will need an acid (lemon juice, vinegar or hydrochloric acid), a straw or glass eyedropper, and a hand lens when working with weaker acids. To test a mineral to see if it is calcite, simply place a drop of the acid onto the surface of the mineral. Use the hand lens to observe the mineral and see if bubbles appear on the surface. If so, then the mineral is made of calcium carbonate, such as calcite. While calcite and aragonite have the strongest reactions to an acid, other common minerals such as chalk, dolomite, magnesite, malachite, azurite and rhodochrosite will exhibit weak reactions as well.

2.11   *Gemstones*

A gemstone is a mineral that has a superior brilliance, luster and rarity that makes them highly valuable. Typically, rough samples of the gemstone, such as the ruby on the left, do not have the brilliant appearance as the cut and polished ruby, shown on the right.

Scientists classify gemstones as precious and semi-precious. Precious stones are rarer than semi-precious. Gemstones are common in jewelry and collections. Precious gemstones include diamonds, rubies, sapphires and emeralds. Interestingly, the gemstones ruby and sapphire are both forms of the corundum mineral. The difference in the ruby and sapphire varieties are trace elements in the chemical formula of the gemstone. Chromium causes the red color of rubies while sapphire forms in a variety of colors due to traces of iron, titanium and chromium in the crystal. Similarly, emeralds are a green form of the mineral beryl, while the semi-precious aquamarine gemstone is another variety of the same mineral.

2.12   *Mineral Uses*

Minerals have many uses in our lives. Ask students to name how many minerals they use every day. Here are some common uses of minerals.

Mineral	Common Use
Talc	Baby powder
Graphite	Pencil lead
Galena	Lead content. Lead is used in many household items.
Lepidolite	Lithium content. Lithium can be used in medicine and in the production of atomic energy.
Rhodonite	Jewelry
Limonite	Yellow & brown dyes and pigments
Tourmaline	Jewelry and high-pressure gauges
Epidote	Jewelry and collecting
Amazonite	Jewelry and collecting
Malachite	Jewelry
Quartz	Prisms, lenses, gauges, glass, paints and abrasives
Azurite	Blue dyes and pigments
Beryl	Jewelry (Green is Emerald, Blue is Aquamarine)
Calcite	Microscopes, building materials, metallurgy, fertilizers and chemical industry
Fluorite	Enamels, cooking utensils, telescopes, camera lenses
Gypsum	Paints, tile, drywall, blackboard chalk, fertilizer, plater of paris
Halite	Salt for food preparation and in the chemical industry
Hematite	Jewelry, red pigments, plate-glass
Limonite	Dyes and pigments
Pyrite	Sulfuric acid production

2.13   *Suggested Mineral Identification Exercises*

Mineral identification is a fun exercise for students because there are so many tests they can perform. The Mineral Identification Flow Chart in Appendix A is designed for younger students and beginners and will help them identify the minerals based on only a few characteristics. Appendix B provides a Mineral Property Record Sheet which all students may use to record their observations of each of their samples during the identification process. You can also use the Common Mineral Information sheets from Appendix C to provide the students with additional information about each mineral, which will allow them to perform additional tests.

Older and/or more experienced students may enjoy performing multiple tests on each sample, recording the results and finding the sample using the Common Mineral Information sheets only.

Elementary Students

For elementary students, limit sample groups to two minerals of each outward color or each streak color that have a distinguishing property between them. For example, you can use a white calcite and a green fluorite that both have white streak colors. They look very similar but their distinguishing characteristic is that calcite will fizz if you place an acid, like vinegar or lemon juice, on the sample. The following are some suggested pairs for mineral identification for elementary students:

Group 1	Group 2	Group 3	Group 4	Group 5
Fluorite	Magnetite	Gypsum	Halite	Beryl
Calcite	Augite	Amethyst	Olivine	Sodalite

Middle and High School Students

Middle and high school students are old enough to learn to distinguish between similar minerals. As long as you have high-quality samples and the information about the properties of each, allow students to attempt to identify larger sample sets. Have students record each of the properties such as color, luster, hardness, streak and shape, in order to compare against the information given for each mineral on the Mineral Property Record Sheet included in the Appendix. Other properties that may be helpful are density, magnetism, and the reaction to acid. Middle and high school students can also use the flow chart to identify their sample using the properties that they determine for each mineral. The following are some suggested groups for mineral identification for middle and high school students:

Group 1	Group 2	Group 3	Group 4	Group 5
Beryl	Gypsum	Azurite	Magnetite	Clear Quartz
Olivine	Halite	Kyanite	Augite	Amethyst
Green Fluorite	Calcite	Malachite	Biotite Mica	Milky Quartz
Amazonite Feldspar	White/Clear Fluorite	Sodalite	Garnet	Microcline Feldspar

CHAPTER 3

IGNEOUS ROCK IDENTIFICATION

All rocks are made of one or more minerals. Igneous rocks are some of the oldest rocks on Earth and form in volcanic areas from magma and lava. Magma is hot, molten rock that is under the surface of the Earth. Lava is hot, molten rock that erupted from a volcano or cracks in the crust and is on the surface of the Earth. The chemical composition of the magma or lava and the method used to form the rock determine the type of igneous rock that results.

3.1   Igneous Rock Formation

Igneous rocks form from magma, a mixture of gas, crystals and melted rock, located deep underground. In general, there are two types of igneous rocks that students should understand. These two types are:

Fast Cooling
Small or No Crystals

Slow Cooling
Medium to Large Crystals

Extrusive Rocks are formed when magma is ejected (thrown) from the volcano and cools above ground. Usually, these rocks have no crystals or small crystals because the rocks cool quickly and there is not much time for crystals to grow. Examples of extrusive rocks are scoria, obsidian and basalt.

FAST COOLING = NO CRYSTALS OR SMALL CRYSTALS

Intrusive Rocks are formed when magma remains underground in mass or is injected into cracks in rocks and cools slowly. Usually, intrusive rocks have medium to large sized crystals because the magma cools slowly and the crystals have time to form larger sizes. Examples of intrusive rocks are granite, pegmatite and gabbro.

SLOW COOLING = MEDIUM TO LARGE CRYSTALS

Magma is a mixture of different elements that form the minerals in rocks. Magmas in different areas of the world can have different mixtures. The majority of the rocks on the Earth are made of the elements silicon, aluminum, iron, calcium, magnesium, potassium, sodium, and oxygen. The type of igneous rocks that form at each location depends on the amount of these elements present in the magma and the minerals that will form from the mixture.

There are three common magma types including basaltic, andesitic and rhyolitic. The following is a summary of the properties of each magma type.

Type of Magma	Common Extrusive Rock Formed	Common Instrusive Rock Formed	Common Elements and Compounds in Magma	Magma Viscosity/Magma Temperature/Rock Color
Rhyolitic	Rhyolite	Granite	High SiO2, K, Na. Low in other common elements	High/Low/Light
Andesitic	Andesite	Diorite	Moderate SiO2 and other common elements	Moderate/Moderate/Often speckled light and dark
Basaltic	Basalt	Gabbro	Low SiO2, K, Na. High in other common elements	Low/High/Dark

It is not necessary for elementary students to understand the variety of magmas but it can be a fun exercise for them to try to match rocks to possible magma types based on the color of the minerals present.

INTERESTING FACT:	Look at samples of granite and obsidian. These two rocks were made from magma with the same mineral mixture. One rock is extrusive and one rock is intrusive. Can you see the difference in the crystal sizes? The obsidian cools so quickly that it looks like black glass and you cannot see the crystals of quartz, feldspar and mica that you can see in the granite which cooled slowly.

3.2   Volcanoes

Volcanoes are areas where the rock is built up around an opening in the Earth which connects the land surface to the magma below the ground surface. When the pressure deep below the volcano increases, the magma erupts and is ejected from below ground to the land's surface. Three of the most common types of volcanoes for students to understand are:

Kilauea Volcano in Hawaii Volcanoes National Park

SHIELD VOLCANOES

Shield volcanoes get their name because they are usually a wide mound, similar in appearance to a knight's shield. These volcanoes are very large and relatively flat compared to other types of volcanoes. Shield volcanoes do not have violent eruptions. When a shield volcano erupts, the lava pours out of the vent hole in the top and spreads over the volcanic rocks surrounding the vent. The Hawaiian Islands are made up of a line of shield volcanoes. Magma associated with shield volcanoes is often basaltic.

STRATOVOLCANOES (ALSO CALLED COMPOSITE VOLCANOES)

North ridge of
Mount St. Helens

Stratovolcanoes form tall mountains. Layers of lava, cinders, ash and rock build up the mountain from violent eruptions. During an eruption, lava may flow out of the opening at the top of the volcano but may also release from cracks in the side of the volcano too. Mount St. Helens, located in Washington State, is a stratovolcano. Magma associated with stratovolcanoes is often andesitic or rhyolitic.

CINDER CONES

Sunset Crater Volcano in
northern Arizona

A cinder cone is the simplest form of a volcano. Lava erupts violently from the volcano and forms cinders (scoria) which fall back to the earth on top of the cone, making it larger. Cinder cones often form next to other volcanoes and are typically smaller. Sunset Crater in Arizona is a well-known cinder cone. Magmas associated with cinder cone volcanoes are often basaltic or andesitic.

3.3   *Igneous Rock Textures*

The texture of an igneous rock describes the size of the crystals in the sample. Textures can be described as: 1) having no crystals with a glassy or vesicular (with holes) texture, 2) fine-grained with tiny crystals that are difficult to see with the naked eye, 3) medium-grained with grains that you can distinguish with the naked eye, 4) coarse-grained with large crystals that are easy to see, and 5) porphyritic with two distinct crystal sizes in one rock.

The first step in igneous rock identification is determining the texture. Generally, rocks with no crystals or fine grains are extrusive rocks that form outside of the volcano. Rocks with medium or coarse grains form underground where the cooling time was slow. Porphyritic textures form when the rock begins to cool below ground forming large crystals and later erupts from the volcano allowing the remaining magma to cool quickly and form a fine-grained rock with the larger grains trapped inside.

Examples of each texture type are summarized in the chart.

NO CRYSTALS The rock does not have any crystals. These rocks are either Glassy or Vesicular.		**GLASSY:** Obsidian The rock looks like a piece of colored glass.		**VESICULAR:** Scoria The rock has no crystals but has many, many tiny holes.
FINE-GRAINED The crystals are so tiny you can not see each individual crystal.		RHYOLITE
MEDIUM-GRAINED The crystals are medium-sized so you can see the individual grains.		GRANITE
COARSE-GRAINED The crystals are very large and can easily be seen.		PEGMATITE
PORPHYRITIC There are two different sizes of crystal in the rock. The large grains appear to be "floating" inside the rest of the rock.		VOLCANIC BRECCIA

3.4   Mineral Content, Color and Special Features of Igneous Rocks

The color of igneous rocks is controlled by the composition of the magma. Light colored rocks are generally rhyolitic magmas while dark rocks are generally basaltic magmas. Rocks with all light colored minerals will be light in color, like quartzite, while a rock made of all dark minerals will be dark in color, like gabbro. Andesitic magmas often produce rocks with light and dark minerals, so they are often speckled.

The type of igneous rock is dictated by the mineral content. Geologists often classify *major minerals* as the dominant minerals in the rock and *minor minerals* as the accessory minerals that are less important in the rock type. The major minerals and their relative percentages determine the type of rock. Geologists do not consider minor minerals as much when determining igneous rock types.

Just as you can divide rocks by mineral content, texture and color, you can use special properties of rocks to help determine their identity. For example, some rocks, like obsidian, look like glass, while others, like pumice and scoria, have holes. In addition, some igneous rocks can float on water while others will sink.

3.5   Igneous Rock Uses

Just like minerals, igneous rocks have many uses in our daily lives. One of the most common uses of igneous rocks is for road building and construction. Crushed granite is a common road bed construction material and you can also find granite inside buildings as counter top and even wall tiles. Homeowners will often use pieces of scoria in flower beds around their home and pumice is known as a common rock for beauty products such as foot smoothing stones and in soap. Most students should be able to find one use of an igneous rock in their home or community.

3.6   Suggested Igneous Rock Identification Exercises

Igneous Rock identification is enjoyable for students because the appearance of the samples can vary widely and most children are interested in volcanoes and figuring out which rocks were made underground and which formed above ground. The Igneous Rock Identification Flow Chart in Appendix A is designed for younger students and beginners and will help them identify the minerals based on only a few characteristics. However, you can use the Igneous Rock Property Identification Cards from Appendix C to provide the students with additional information about each mineral, which will allow them to perform additional tests.

Older and/or more experienced students may enjoy performing multiple tests on each sample, recording the results and finding the sample using the Igneous Rock Property Identification Cards. Appendix B provides an Igneous Rock Property Record Sheet which all students may use to record their observations of each of their samples during the identification process.

Elementary Students

For elementary students, limit sample groups to two igneous rocks at a time. Make sure the rocks have at least one similarity and, at least, one difference so students can see how rocks that look very similar actually have at least one property that distinguishes them from others. The following are some suggested pairs for igneous rocks identification for elementary students:

Group 1	Group 2	Group 3	Group 4	Group 5
Obsidian	Rhyolite	Trachyte	Gabbro	Syenite
Basalt	Scoria	Volcanic Breccia	Diorite	Pegmatite

Middle and High School Students

Middle and high school students are old enough to learn to distinguish between multiple similar igneous rocks. As long as you have high-quality samples and the information about the properties of each, allow students to attempt to identify larger sample sets. Have students record the properties of each sample on the Igneous Rock Property Record Sheet included in the Appendix. Students can use these properties to follow the flow chart to identify each sample. The following are some suggested groups for igneous rocks identification for middle and high school students:

Group 1	Group 2	Group 3	Group 4	Group 5
Obsidian	Carbonatite	Trachyte	Peridotite	Monzonite
Basalt	Pumice	Andesite	Gabbro	Syenite
Snowflake Obsidian	Scoria	Volcanic Breccia	Diorite	Anorthosite
-	Rhyolite	-	Granite	Pegmatite

CHAPTER 4

SEDIMENTARY ROCK IDENTIFICATION

S edimentary rocks form from sediments such as sand, silt or clay. There are many places where a sedimentary rock can form such as rivers, lakes, oceans and deserts. Sedimentary rocks have several methods of formation and some unique features that no other rocks types exhibit.

4.1   *Sedimentary Rock Formation*

Sedimentary rocks form from several different processes, such as compression, evaporation, chemical precipitation or from organics.

COMPRESSION: Compression is the squeezing of sediments together to make rocks. This method usually forms rocks like sandstone and shale when layers of sediments such as sand and clay are deposited on top of each other. These layers are buried by more layers of sediment. As new layers deposit on top, the bottom layers compress (squeeze) together until they form a hard rock. These rocks may have obvious or subtle layers that you can see.

EVAPORATION: Sedimentary rocks that form by evaporation form in large areas such as lakes or oceans. These types of rocks are left behind when the water evaporates. Rock salt is a common rock that forms by evaporation.

CHEMICAL PRECIPITATION: Chemical precipitation means that dissolved minerals in a water body or water source will separate from the water and become solid rock. Limestone is a common sedimentary rock that can form by precipitation. Dissolved calcite, calcium carbonate, in water will precipitate to form limestone. Limestone can form in any water body and can also form in caves and create formations within cave openings.

ORGANICS: Coal is an example of an organic sedimentary rock. Organic rocks form from living things, like plants. When plant material, like trees or bushes, die in swampy areas, layers of sediment and additional dead organics cover the plant material and bury it below the land's surface. As the depth of the dead plant material increases below ground, high heat and pressure turn the buried plant material into coal.

INTERESTING FACT:	Sandstone is a unique sedimentary rock because tiny holes stay between the sand grains of the new rock as it forms. These little holes can store water, natural gas and oil underground.

4.2   *Sedimentary Rock Textures and Grain Sizes*

The textures of sedimentary rocks are similar to that of igneous rocks. The texture of a sedimentary rock describes the size of the crystals in the sample. Geologists describe sedimentary rock textures as: 1) having no crystals that are rocks made of organic material or cemented shell fragments, 2) fine-grained with tiny crystals that are difficult to see with the naked eye, 3) medium-grained with grains that you can distinguish with the naked eye, and 4) coarse-grained with large crystals that are easy to see.

The following table provides the names of many common sediment/grain types, the sizes, and texture of the sediment and the rocks it typically forms.

Grain Type	Particle Size	Common Texture Classification	Common Sedimentary Rock
Clay	<1/256 mm	Fine-grained	Shale
Silt	1/256 - 1/16 mm	Fine to Medium-grained	Siltstone
Sand	1/16 - 2 mm	Medium-grained	Sandstone
Pebble	2 - 64 mm	Medium to Coarse-grained	Conglmerate and Breccia
Cobble	64 - 256 mm	Coarse-grained	
Boulder	>256 mm	Coarse-grained	

The first step in sedimentary rock identification is determining the texture. Common rocks associated with each sedimentary texture type are summarized in the chart below.

NO CRYSTALS
The rock does not have any crystals.
These rocks are either Organic or Shelly.

ORGANIC: Coal
The rock is made
from plants.

SHELLY: Coquina
The rock is made of
mostly shell pieces.

FINE-GRAINED
The mineral crystals are so small that you can not see individual crystals without a microscope.

SHALE

MEDIUM-GRAINED
The mineral crystals are large enough to be seen without a microscope but the crystals are not huge.

SANDSTONE

COARSE-GRAINED
The mineral crystals can easily be seen without a microscope and are very large.

BRECCIA

4.3   Special Features of Sedimentary Rocks

Sedimentary rocks often contain calcite and fossils. Rocks that contain calcite are known as limestone. You can use an acid test to determine if your sample contains calcite. In addition, sedimentary rocks are the only type of rock to contain fossils. These fossils give you a clue to the type of sedimentary rock you have, as well as the method of its formation.

The Fizz Test for Limestone Rocks

Many sedimentary rocks can look alike. Sometimes telling the difference between limestone, shale or silt-stone can be difficult. One way geologists test the rocks is by performing the acid or "Fizz Test" that we discussed in the mineral section. Calcite is the main component of limestone rocks and its varieties like oolitic limestone, fossiliferous limestone and coquina. The calcite mineral is made of calcium carbonate which reacts with acid. To perform the test you will need an acid (lemon juice, vinegar or hydrochloric acid), a straw or glass eyedropper, and a hand lens when working with weaker acids. To test a rock to see if it is calcite, simply place a drop of the acid onto the surface of the rock in the same manner as you would a mineral sample. Because rocks can have impurities or more than one mineral, have the students test several areas on the rock sample and use a hand lens to closely observe the bubbles.

The Fossil Record

Sedimentary rocks sometimes have a unique feature that neither igneous nor metamorphic have...*FOSSILS!* Fossils are bits of animals or plants that are preserved in a rock as it forms. Dinosaur bones, seashells and plant leaves often exist in limestone and shale. Fossils can also be imprints of animals or plants like dinosaur footprints.

Fossils usually form in quiet places where the rocks form without being disturbed by waves or the wind (such as an ocean or lake floor) or where the layers of rock were deposited quickly and the animal or plant was buried rapidly without being disturbed (such as a river, lake or desert). As the layers harden, rock forms with the fossil inside.

For example, a sea shell may drop to the bottom of the ocean in a deep area without waves. Sediment then covers and buries the sea shell. Over time, the sediment layers, with the seashell inside, compress into a rock. That seashell becomes a fossil!

 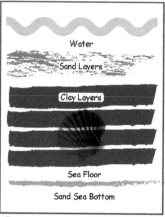 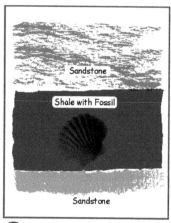

① A sea shell may drop to the bottom of the ocean in a deep area without waves. The sea shell is covered with sediment and buried.

② Over time, the sediment layers, with the sea shell inside, are compressed into a rock.

③ That sea shell becomes a fossil!

Sedimentary rocks that contain fossils help geologists understand the time and method of formation. For example, fossiliferous limestone is a variety of limestone that is generally fine-grained and has fossil impressions or shells encased within the rock. The presence of a fossil in a rock is a clue to the fact that it is sedimentary and the fizz test can help conclude if the rock is a limestone. Shale is another sedimentary rock that often contains fossils and can help a geologist understand the history of an area. The location of the shale, even if on land today, tells geologists that the area was likely as ocean setting in the past.

4.4 Sedimentary Rock Uses

Sedimentary rocks also have many uses in our daily lives. Coal is a fuel source and many power companies burn coal to power our homes and businesses. Construction workers may use other sedimentary rocks such as sandstone, limestone and coquina as building materials although they are not always as durable as some igneous and metamorphic rocks. If you wander through a home good store you can often find sedimentary rocks in the form of decorative accessories such as coasters, statues and garden furniture.

4.5   Suggested Sedimentary Rock Identification Exercises

Sedimentary Rock identification is enjoyable for students because the rocks can have very different methods of formation and may contain fossils. The Sedimentary Rock Identification Flow Chart in Appendix A is designed for younger students and beginners and will help them identify the minerals based on only a few characteristics. However, you can use the Sedimentary Rock Property Identification Cards from Appendix C to provide the students with additional information about each mineral, which will allow them to perform additional tests.

Older and/or more experienced students may enjoy performing multiple tests on each sample, recording the results and finding the sample using the Sedimentary Rock Property Identification Cards. Appendix B provides a Sedimentary Rock Property Record Sheet which all students may use to record their observations of each of their samples during the identification process.

Elementary Students

For elementary students, limit sample groups to two sedimentary rocks at a time. Make sure the rocks have at least one similarity and, at least, one difference so they can see how rocks that look close to the same actually have something that distinguishes them. Many sedimentary rocks look very much alike, so allow students time to identify the rocks. The following are some suggested pairs for sedimentary rock identification for elementary students:

Group 1	Group 2	Group 3	Group 4
Bituminous Coal	Shale	Fossiliferous Limestone	Congolmerate
Coquina	Limestone	Siltstone	Sandstone

Middle and High School Students

Middle and high school students are old enough to learn to distinguish between multiple similar sedimentary rocks. As long as you have high-quality samples and the information about the properties of each, allow students to attempt to identify larger sample sets. Have students record the properties of each sample on the Sedimentary Rock Property Record Sheet included in the Appendix. Students can use these properties to follow the flow chart to identify each sample. The following are some suggested groups for sedimentary rock identification for middle and high school students:

Group 1	Group 2	Group 3	Group 4
Bituminous Coal	Shale	Oolitic Limestone	Conglomerate
Lignite Coal	Loess	Fossiliferous Limestone	Sedimentary Breccia
Coquina	Limestone	Siltstone	Sandstone
-	-	-	Arkose

CHAPTER 5

METAMORPHIC ROCK IDENTIFICATION

The third type of rock that makes up our Earth is metamorphic. Metamorphic rocks are the rocks that change either physically or chemically by heat, pressure and/or hot fluids. The term metamorphic comes from the Greek words "meta," which means change, and "morph," which means form. Metamorphism is a solid state change, meaning that the minerals within the rock recrystallize in response to heat, pressure and the chemical reaction with hot fluids without melting the original rock.

5.1   Metamorphic Rock Formation

Metamorphic rocks are rocks that once were sedimentary or igneous rocks but changed because they were heated and/or squeezed. The rocks get exposed to high temperature, high pressure, and/or hot, mineral-rich fluids as they are buried or moved deeper below the Earth's crust. Some examples of metamorphic rocks are:

Metamorphic rocks have many uses such as construction materials for roads, buildings, roofs, jewelry and statues, to name a few. Usually, a rock is metamorphosed (changed) when the temperature of the rock is between 300°F and 2000°F or when it is deeper than 12 miles below the surface of the Earth. The temperatures and pressures at this depth cause the rock to change by allowing the minerals to change into different forms without melting. The new rock may also have a different texture than the old rock. The changing of sedimentary and igneous rocks into metamorphic rocks is part of the Rock Cycle.

INTERESTING FACT:	When a sedimentary rock changes into a metamorphic rock, the heat and pressure destroys almost all of the fossils in the rock.

5.2   Types of Metamorphism

Metamorphism happens deep in the earth's crust. There are many types of metamorphism that geologists talk about but four general types that students should understand are:

HORNFELS

CONTACT METAMORPHISM: Contact metamorphism is caused by high heat and/or circulating waters. This type of metamorphism happens near magma sources (near volcanoes and deep underground). Only the rocks along the edges of the magma are heated and changed; therefore, contact metamorphism occurs over a small area. Hornfels is a common contact metamorphic rock.

GNEISS

REGIONAL METAMORPHISM: Regional metamorphism is caused by high heat and high pressure. This type of metamorphism happens over very large areas as layers of rock and sediment bury the original rocks far below the surface of the Earth. Regional metamorphism often occurs along plate boundaries and in areas with significant sediment and rock layer deposition. This type of metamorphism often happens over huge areas that are greater 1,000 square miles and may be associated with mountain building. Slate, schist and gneiss are common regional metamorphic rocks. Some rocks, like marble and quartzite, can form from both contact and regional metamorphism.

MARBLE

CATACLASTIC METAMORPHISM occurs along fault zones from intense pressure. This type of metamorphism involves brittle deformation which is where the rocks break into small pieces.

HYDROTHERMAL METAMORPHISM occurs when hot, mineral-rich waters alter the existing rock. Generally, this type of metamorphism occurs in areas of low temperature and low pressure.

5.3   Metamorphic Rock Textures

The textures of metamorphic rocks are similar to that of igneous and sedimentary rocks. The texture of a metamorphic rock describes the size of the crystals in the sample. Textures can be described as: 1) having no crystals that are made of organic material, 2) fine-grained with tiny crystals that are difficult to see with the naked eye, 3) medium-grained with grains that you can distinguish with the naked eye, and 4) coarse-grained with large crystals that are easy to see. The following chart gives examples of metamorphic rock textures.

NO CRYSTALS The rock does not have any crystals. These rocks are usually organic which means the rock is made from plants. ORGANIC: Coal The rock is made from plants.	**FINE-GRAINED** The mineral crystals are so small that you can not see individual crystals without a microscope. SLATE
MEDIUM-GRAINED The mineral crystals are large enough to be seen without a microscope but the crystals are not huge. MARBLE	**COARSE-GRAINED** The mineral crystals can easily be seen without a microscope and are very large. GNEISS

Foliation

Another distinguishing feature of metamorphic rocks is foliation. Geologists classify some metamorphic rock as foliated and others as non-foliated or granular. Foliated metamorphic rocks have a banded look to them. This banding, or layering, is due to mineral grains lining up during metamorphism from the heat and high pressure that squeezed the rock together. Non-foliated, or granular, rocks do not appear banded, but rather look like a mass of mineral grains. Granular rocks often have one mineral as the main component, like marble and quartzite.

5.4 *Special Features of Metamorphic Rocks*

Index Minerals

Certain minerals, called "Index Minerals," form in metamorphic rocks as the temperature and pressure of the rock increases. Geologists study these minerals so when they see them, they know how high the temperature and pressure were when the rocks formed. These index minerals are another clue to the Earth's past. This table shows the index minerals and the order in which they form in metamorphic rocks.

Order	Index Mineral		Temperature and Pressure
First to Form	Chlorite		
Second to Form	Muscovite ——▶		Low Temperature and Pressure
Third to Form	Biotite		
Fourth to Form	Hornblende		
Fifth to Form	Garnet ——▶		Medium Temperature and Pressure
Sixth to Form	Staurolite		
Seventh to Form	Kyanite ——▶		High Temperature and Pressure
Eighth to Form	Sillimanite		

Acid Reaction

As discussed in the sections on minerals and sedimentary rocks, calcite-containing rocks will react when exposed to an acid. Metamorphic rocks, such as marble, can contain calcite and will also react to acid. To test a metamorphic rock for calcite content, you perform the test in the same manner described in the previous sections.

Interlocking Grains

The metamorphic processes of high heat and high temperature can cause mineral grains to become interlocked with surrounding crystal. For example, quartzite is a metamorphic rock that was once quartz sandstone. The quartz sandstone changes to quartzite from high heat and pressure deep inside the Earth. Sometimes quartzite rocks have the same outward appearance as the original sandstone, making the two rocks difficult to tell apart. In quartzite, the sand grains are interlocking, but in sandstone, they are simply "glued" together with quartz cement.

So, how do you tell them apart? Interestingly, there is one way to tell these rocks apart and it is fun to do! Wrap the rocks in a towel and place them on a sturdy table or on the floor. Wearing safety goggles, break each rock sample using a rock hammer. Use a hand magnifier to examine each rock along the breaks made with the hammer. The sandstone will break *around* the quartz sand grains, so you will be able to see individual, whole grains. The quartzite will fracture *through* the quartz sand grains so you will not see individual, whole grains.

5.5 Metamorphic Rock Uses

Metamorphic rocks also have many uses in our homes and communities. Metamorphic coal is a fuel source just like the sedimentary varieties; however, metamorphic coal gives off the most heat of any coal during the burning process. Many metamorphic rocks, like gneiss and marble, are common building materials. Slate is common as flooring and roofing material, as well as blackboards.

5.6 Suggested Metamorphic Rock Identification Exercises

Metamorphic Rock identification is enjoyable for students because the rocks can have different methods of formation and may, on occasion, contain fossils. The Metamorphic Rock Identification Flow Chart in Appendix A is designed for younger students and beginners and will help them identify the minerals based on only a few characteristics. However, you can use the Metamorphic Rock Property Identification Cards from Appendix C to provide the students with additional information about each mineral, which will allow them to perform additional tests.

Older and/or more experienced students may enjoy performing multiple tests on each sample, recording the results and finding the sample using the Metamorphic Rock Property Identification Cards. Appendix B provides a Metamorphic Rock Property Record Sheet, which all students may use to record their observations of each of their samples during the identification process.

Elementary Students

For elementary students, limit sample groups to two metamorphic rocks at a time. Make sure the rocks have at least one similarity and, at least, one difference so they can see how even rocks that look close to the same actually have something that distinguishes them. The following are some suggested pairs for metamorphic rocks identification for elementary students:

Group 1	Group 2	Group 3	Group 4
Anthracite Coal	Garnet Schist	Gneiss	Quartzite
Slate	Phyllite	Marble	Amphibolite

Middle and High School Students

Middle and high school students are old enough to learn to distinguish between multiple similar metamorphic rocks. As long as you have high-quality samples and the information about the properties of each, allow students to attempt to identify large sample sets. Have students record the properties of each sample on the Metamorphic Rock Property Record Sheet included in the Appendix. Students can use these properties to follow the flow chart to identify each sample.

The following are some suggested groups for metamorphic rocks identification for middle and high school students:

Group 1	Group 2	Group 3	Group 4
Anthracite Coal	Mica Schist	Amphibolite	White Marble
Hornfels	Garnet Schist	Gneiss	White Quartzite
Slate	Tourmaline Schist	Granitiod Gneiss	Pink Marble
–	Phyllite	–	Pink Quartzite

CHAPTER 6

THE ROCK CYCLE

To complete a study of rocks and minerals, students should begin to understand the Rock Cycle. This section gives a brief overview of the cycle and an exercise that you can perform with students to help them understand how rocks form from minerals and other rocks.

6.1   *The Rock Cycle Process*

All of the Earth's rocks are created and destroyed every day in a slow process called the Rock Cycle. Igneous and metamorphic rocks break down from wind and water and can form into sedimentary rocks. Igneous and sedimentary rocks are buried, heated, squeezed and changed into metamorphic rocks. And metamorphic and sedimentary rocks can move into deep, volcanic areas, melt and turn into igneous rocks. The diagram below illustrates the different processes that occur during the Rock Cycle.

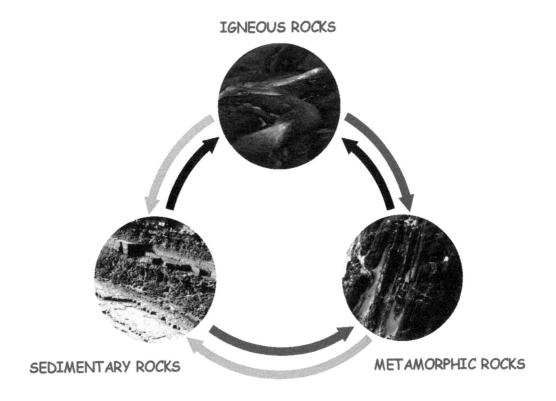

IGNEOUS ROCKS

SEDIMENTARY ROCKS

METAMORPHIC ROCKS

6.2   ***Suggested Rock Cycle Exercise***

Elementary, middle and high school students can benefit from examining the rock cycle process by closely examining the similarities and difference in samples. For this exercise, give students the following chart and several rock and mineral samples. Beginning with the top rock or mineral group, ask students what would be the next logical step in the rock cycle and what process would happen to make this occur.

The Rock Cycle Process

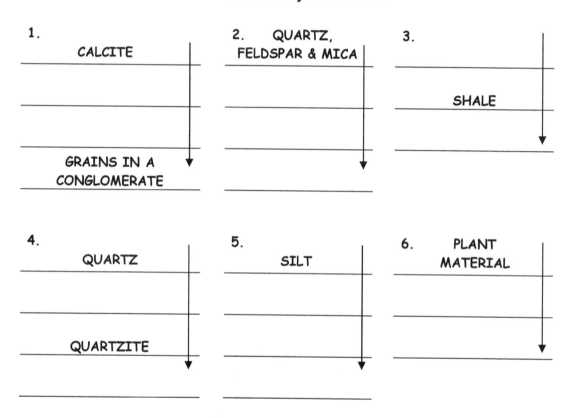

The Rock Cycle Process – Answer Key

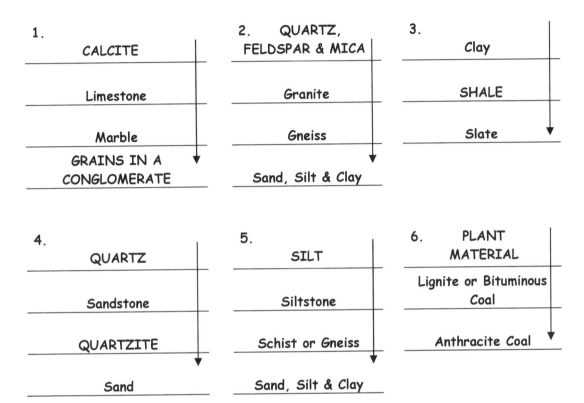

1.

CALCITE

Limestone

Marble

GRAINS IN A CONGLOMERATE

2. QUARTZ, FELDSPAR & MICA

Granite

Gneiss

Sand, Silt & Clay

3.

Clay

SHALE

Slate

4.

QUARTZ

Sandstone

QUARTZITE

Sand

5.

SILT

Siltstone

Schist or Gneiss

Sand, Silt & Clay

6. PLANT MATERIAL

Lignite or Bituminous Coal

Anthracite Coal

Appendix A

Mineral & Rock Identification Flow Charts

MINERAL IDENTIFICATON FLOW CHART

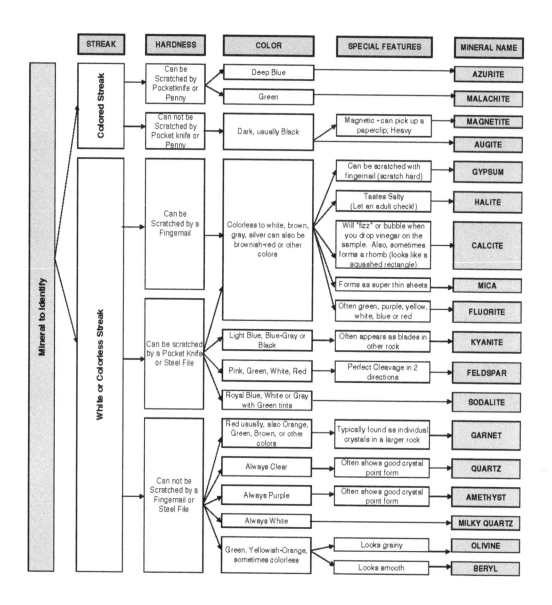

IGNEOUS ROCK IDENTIFICATON FLOW CHART

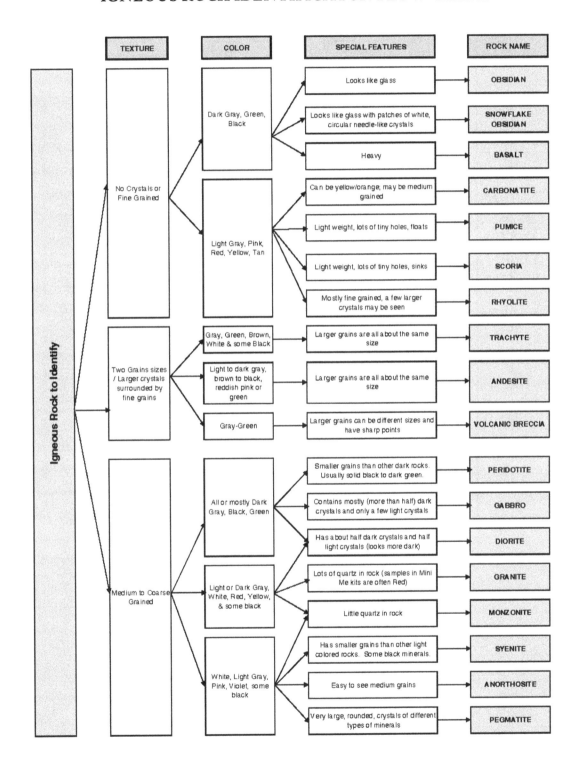

SEDIMENTARY ROCK IDENTIFICATON FLOW CHART

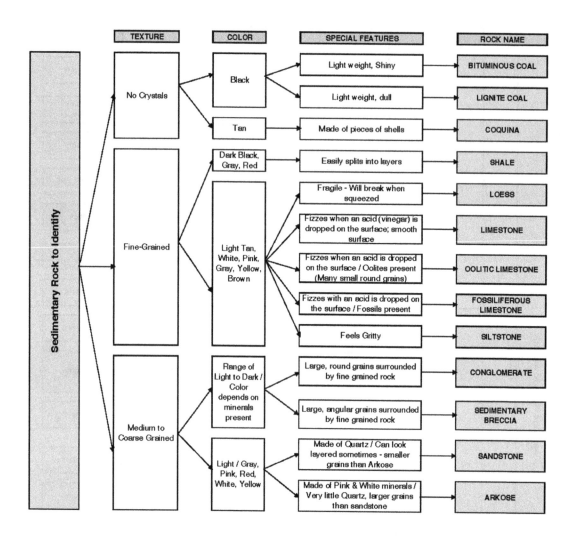

METAMORPHIC ROCK IDENTIFICATON FLOW CHART

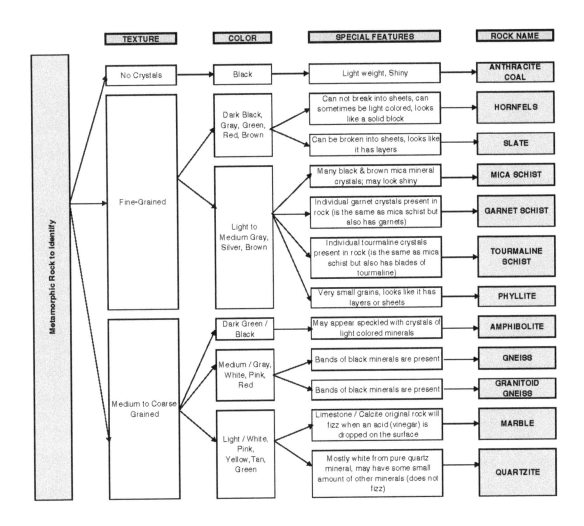

APPENDIX B

Mineral & Rock Property
Record Sheets

Mineral Property Record Sheet

Sample ID Number _____

Color _____

Streak _____

Hardness _____

Luster _____

Cleavage _____

Fracture _____

Special Features _____

Sample Name _____

Sample ID Number _____

Color _____

Streak _____

Hardness _____

Luster _____

Cleavage _____

Fracture _____

Special Features _____

Sample Name _____

Sample ID Number _____

Color _____

Streak _____

Hardness _____

Luster _____

Cleavage _____

Fracture _____

Special Features _____

Sample Name _____

Sample ID Number _____

Color _____

Streak _____

Hardness _____

Luster _____

Cleavage _____

Fracture _____

Special Features _____

Sample Name _____

Sample ID Number _____

Color _____

Streak _____

Hardness _____

Luster _____

Cleavage _____

Fracture _____

Special Features _____

Sample Name _____

Sample ID Number _____

Color _____

Streak _____

Hardness _____

Luster _____

Cleavage _____

Fracture _____

Special Features _____

Sample Name _____

Sample ID Number _____

Color _____

Streak _____

Hardness _____

Luster _____

Cleavage _____

Fracture _____

Special Features _____

Sample Name _____

Sample ID Number _____

Color _____

Streak _____

Hardness _____

Luster _____

Cleavage _____

Fracture _____

Special Features _____

Sample Name _____

Igneous Rock Property Record Sheet

Sample ID Number _____

Color _____

Texture/Minerals _____

Magma Type _____

Intrusive / Extrusive _____

Special Features _____

Sample Name _____

Sample ID Number _____

Color _____

Texture/Minerals _____

Magma Type _____

Intrusive / Extrusive _____

Special Features _____

Sample Name _____

Sample ID Number _____

Color _____

Texture/Minerals _____

Magma Type _____

Intrusive / Extrusive _____

Special Features _____

Sample Name _____

Sample ID Number _____

Color _____

Texture/Minerals _____

Magma Type _____

Intrusive / Extrusive _____

Special Features _____

Sample Name _____

Sample ID Number _____

Color _____

Texture/Minerals _____

Magma Type _____

Intrusive / Extrusive _____

Special Features _____

Sample Name _____

Sample ID Number _____

Color _____

Texture/Minerals _____

Magma Type _____

Intrusive / Extrusive _____

Special Features _____

Sample Name _____

Sample ID Number _____

Color _____

Texture/Minerals _____

Magma Type _____

Intrusive / Extrusive _____

Special Features _____

Sample Name _____

Sample ID Number _____

Color _____

Texture/Minerals _____

Magma Type _____

Intrusive / Extrusive _____

Special Features _____

Sample Name _____

Sample ID Number _____

Color _____

Texture/Minerals _____

Magma Type _____

Intrusive / Extrusive _____

Special Features _____

Sample Name _____

Sample ID Number _____

Color _____

Texture/Minerals _____

Magma Type _____

Intrusive / Extrusive _____

Special Features _____

Sample Name _____

Sedimentary Rock Property Record Sheet

Sample ID Number _____
Color _____
Texture _____
Grain Type _____
Fossils (yes / no) _____
Special Features _____
Sample Name _____

Sample ID Number _____
Color _____
Texture _____
Grain Type _____
Fossils (yes / no) _____
Special Features _____
Sample Name _____

Sample ID Number _____
Color _____
Texture _____
Grain Type _____
Fossils (yes / no) _____
Special Features _____
Sample Name _____

Sample ID Number _____
Color _____
Texture _____
Grain Type _____
Fossils (yes / no) _____
Special Features _____
Sample Name _____

Sample ID Number _____
Color _____
Texture _____
Grain Type _____
Fossils (yes / no) _____
Special Features _____
Sample Name _____

Sample ID Number _____
Color _____
Texture _____
Grain Type _____
Fossils (yes / no) _____
Special Features _____
Sample Name _____

Sample ID Number _____
Color _____
Texture _____
Grain Type _____
Fossils (yes / no) _____
Special Features _____
Sample Name _____

Sample ID Number _____
Color _____
Texture _____
Grain Type _____
Fossils (yes / no) _____
Special Features _____
Sample Name _____

Sample ID Number _____
Color _____
Texture _____
Grain Type _____
Fossils (yes / no) _____
Special Features _____
Sample Name _____

Sample ID Number _____
Color _____
Texture _____
Grain Type _____
Fossils (yes / no) _____
Special Features _____
Sample Name _____

Metamorphic Rock Property Record Sheet

Sample ID Number _____

Color _____

Texture _____

Index Mineral _____

Former Rock Type _____

Special Features _____

Sample Name _____

Sample ID Number _____

Color _____

Texture _____

Index Mineral _____

Former Rock Type _____

Special Features _____

Sample Name _____

Sample ID Number _____

Color _____

Texture _____

Index Mineral _____

Former Rock Type _____

Special Features _____

Sample Name _____

Sample ID Number _____

Color _____

Texture _____

Index Mineral _____

Former Rock Type _____

Special Features _____

Sample Name _____

Sample ID Number _____

Color _____

Texture _____

Index Mineral _____

Former Rock Type _____

Special Features _____

Sample Name _____

Sample ID Number _____

Color _____

Texture _____

Index Mineral _____

Former Rock Type _____

Special Features _____

Sample Name _____

Sample ID Number _____

Color _____

Texture _____

Index Mineral _____

Former Rock Type _____

Special Features _____

Sample Name _____

Sample ID Number _____

Color _____

Texture _____

Index Mineral _____

Former Rock Type _____

Special Features _____

Sample Name _____

Sample ID Number _____

Color _____

Texture _____

Index Mineral _____

Former Rock Type _____

Special Features _____

Sample Name _____

Sample ID Number _____

Color _____

Texture _____

Index Mineral _____

Former Rock Type _____

Special Features _____

Sample Name _____

APPENDIX C

Common Mineral & Rock Information

Common Mineral Information

AGATE GEODE - MINERAL	**Color:** Red, Brown, Yellow, Gray, Blue, White, Colorless **Crystal Shape:** None **Cleavage:** None **Fracture:** Conchoidal **Hardness:** 7 on Mohs Hardness Scale **Streak:** White **Luster:** Glassy **Density:** 2.6 g/cm^3 **Locations:** Worldwide **Uses:** Agates are used as home accents and collector's specimens. **Features:** Agate is a form of quartz. In agate, the crystals are so small you cannot see them. Agate forms in geodes and is typically formed in sedimentary or igneous rocks when an opening, or hole, in the rock is filled with quartz-rich water. Agate forms in circles in the inside of the opening and sometimes larger, prismatic quartz crystals form in the center. "Oco Eggs" is a common term for agate geodes.
AMETHYST - MINERAL	**Color:** Purple **Crystal Shape:** Hexagonal prismatic crystal with a hexagonal pyramid on each end **Cleavage:** None **Fracture:** Conchoidal **Hardness:** 7 on Mohs Hardness Scale **Streak:** White **Luster:** Glassy **Density:** 2.66 g/cm^3 **Locations:** Brazil, Uruguay, Russia, India, Sri Lanka, and United States **Uses:** Amethyst is most commonly used for gemstones in jewelry. **Features:** Purple form of quartz. Amethysts are common in geodes. The purple color is from the presence of ferric iron in the crystal.
APATITE - MINERAL	**Color:** Colorless, Yellow, Green, Brown, Red, Blue **Crystal Shape:** Hexagonal Prismatic Crystals, Masses **Cleavage:** None **Fracture:** Conchoidal **Hardness:** 5 on Mohs Hardness Scale **Streak:** White **Luster:** Glassy to resinous **Density:** 3.1 – 3.2 g/cm^3 **Locations:** Worldwide **Uses:** Phosphate Fertilizer, Salts, Phosphorus **Features:** Heavy and common mineral. Apatite occurs in hydrothermal veins.

ARAGONITE - MINERAL	**Color:** Colorless, White, Yellow, Reddish **Crystal Shape:** Prismatic, often twinned or in rosettes **Cleavage:** 1 Direction (Basal) **Fracture:** Conchoidal **Hardness:** 3.5 to 4 on Mohs Hardness Scale **Streak:** White **Luster:** Glassy **Density:** 2.944 g/cm^3 **Locations:** Spain, United States, Italy, Austria and France **Uses:** Collecting and ornamental stone (alabaster variety). **Features:** Often forms in twins (two crystals together) or clusters (many crystals together). Form of calcium carbonate mineral that will react with acid.
AUGITE - MINERAL	**Color:** Dark Green, Brown or Black **Crystal Shape:** Prismatic, Stubby Crystals, Aggregates **Cleavage:** 2 Directions, 87° **Fracture:** Conchoidal to splintery **Hardness:** 5 to 6 on Mohs Hardness Scale **Streak:** Gray-Green **Luster:** Glassy to Resinous **Density:** 3.31 g/cm^3 **Locations:** South Africa, United States, Greenland **Uses:** Scientific study and collecting **Features:** Heavy, pyroxene mineral. Found in igneous rocks like gabbro and basalt and some metamorphic rocks.
AZURITE - MINERAL	**Color:** Deep Blue **Crystal Shape:** Tabular Prismatic, often intergrown crystals, may also form as a film or in mass **Cleavage:** 3 Directions **Fracture:** Conchoidal **Hardness:** 3.5 to 4 on Mohs Hardness Scale **Streak:** Pale Blue **Luster:** Glassy **Density:** 3.834 g/cm^3 **Locations:** France, Africa, Greece, United States **Uses:** Used as a dye in the past. Sometimes used in beads and jewelry. **Features:** Heavy and fragile. Azurite will fade to green color over time grading to malachite. Crystals may exhibit striations (lines) on flat face. Azurite will react slightly to acid.

BARITE - MINERAL	**Color:** Colorless, Yellow, Red, Green, Black **Crystal Shape:** Tabular, Rosettes, Cockscomb Crystals **Cleavage:** 1 Direction (Basal) **Fracture:** Uneven **Hardness:** 2.5 to 3.5 on Mohs Hardness Scale **Streak:** White **Luster:** Glassy. Sometimes pearly and rarely earthy. **Density:** 4.47 g/cm^3 **Locations:** Crystals over 3 feet long found in England, Transylvania, Czechoslovakia, Romania. Common mineral in other areas of the world including the United States. **Uses:** Drilling mud additive, paints and pigments, medical, paper and rubber industries. **Features:** Very heavy and fragile. Some varieties are fluorescent in ultraviolet light. Barite may form in hydrothermal veins.
BERYL - MINERAL	**Color:** Colorless, Green, Blue, Yellow, Red or White **Crystal Shape:** Prismatic – elongated or flattened **Cleavage:** 1 Direction (Basal) **Fracture:** Conchoidal **Hardness:** 7.5 to 8 on Mohs Hardness Scale **Streak:** White **Luster:** Glassy **Density:** 2.63 – 2.92 g/cm^3 **Locations:** Brazil, India, Russia, Czechoslovakia, Italy, South America, United States **Uses:** Gemstones for jewelry. The green variety is emerald and the blue variety is aquamarine. **Features:** Typically found in granite pegmatite rocks. Most often found in granite pegmatite.
BIOTITE MICA - MINERAL	**Color:** Black, Brown, Greenish-Brown **Crystal Shape:** Thin sheets called "books" **Cleavage:** 1 Direction (Basal) **Fracture:** None due to elasticity of crystal sheets **Hardness:** 2.5 to 3 parallel to crystal face on Mohs Hardness Scale **Streak:** Gray **Luster:** Glassy to pearly **Density:** 2.8 - 3.2 g/cm^3 **Locations:** Italy, United States, Greenland, Scandinavia and Brazil **Uses:** Used in geological study for age dating and collecting. **Features:** Light weight. Forms in very thin sheets and can flake easily. Often found in granite, gneiss, schist and pegmatite and some sedimentary rocks.

CALCITE - MINERAL	**Color:** Colorless, Gray, Red, Yellow, Green, Blue, Violet, Brown or Black **Crystal Shape:** Rhombohedral **Cleavage:** Rhombohedral **Fracture:** Conchoidal **Hardness:** 3 on Mohs Hardness Scale **Streak:** White **Luster:** Glassy to Pearly **Density:** 2.711 g/cm^3 **Locations:** Worldwide **Uses:** Microscopes, Building materials, Metallurgy, Fertilizers and Chemical industry **Features:** Objects viewed through a clear piece, Iceland Spar Calcite, will appear doubled. Calcite forms in water environments or in caves. Reacts strongly to acid.
CHALCEDONY - MINERAL	**Color:** White, Gray, Blue, Brown, or Black **Crystal Shape:** None. May form aggregates and nodules. **Cleavage:** None **Fracture:** Conchoidal **Hardness:** 7 on Mohs Hardness Scale **Streak:** White **Luster:** Waxy to glassy luster depending on the variety **Density:** 2.6 g/cm^3 **Locations:** Worldwide **Uses:** Ornamental stone. Most types can be colored artificially and are easy to polish. **Features:** Usually banded. Chalcedony is a cryptocrystalline form of quartz that precipitates from solution to line rock cavities and fill cracks. This mineral is very hard but lightweight and is transparent when colorless but translucent to opaque with color.
CITRINE - MINERAL	**Color:** Yellowish-Brown, Golden-Brown **Crystal Shape:** Hexagonal prismatic crystal (6-sided barrel) with a hexagonal pyramid on each end **Cleavage:** None **Fracture:** Conchoidal **Hardness:** 7 on Mohs Hardness Scale **Streak:** White **Luster:** Glassy **Density:** 2.66 g/cm^3 **Locations:** Brazil, Russia, France **Uses:** Jewelry **Features:** Yellowish-brown form of quartz. Druze samples form side by side and show nice crystal tips. Amethyst will grade to citrine when heated.

CORUNDUM - MINERAL	**Color:** Gray, Brown, Colorless, Red, Blue, Yellow, Green, Purple **Crystal Shape:** Hexagonal prismatic crystal (6-sided barrel) **Cleavage:** None **Fracture:** Conchoidal **Hardness:** 9 on Mohs Hardness Scale **Streak:** White **Luster:** Glassy or pearly **Density:** 3.997 g/cm^3 **Locations:** Worldwide. Occurs in igneous and metamorphic rocks. **Uses:** Abrasives and Gemstones **Features:** The red variety is the gemstone ruby and the blue variety is sapphire. Corundum is one of the hardest minerals and often forms spotted crystals.
DOLOMITE - MINERAL	**Color:** White, pink, colorless, tan, gray or yellow **Crystal Shape:** Rhombohedron **Cleavage:** Rhombohedral **Fracture:** Conchoidal **Hardness:** 3.5 to 4 on Mohs Hardness scale **Streak:** White **Luster:** Glassy to Pearly **Density:** 2.876 g/cm^3 **Locations:** Worldwide. Nice crystals are found in Italy, Switzerland and United States. **Uses:** Building stone, metallurgy applications and useful to prepare magnesium salts. **Features:** Forms in ocean settings as a sedimentary rock constituent and in hydrothermal veins. Can also be associated with metamorphic rocks. Dolomite will react to an acid but not as strongly as calcite. Dolomite was named after the French mineralogist D. De Dolomieu who lived in the late 1700's.
EPIDOTE - MINERAL	**Color:** Green (the color of pistachio nuts) **Crystal Shape:** Prismatic- elongated, also fibrous **Cleavage:** 1 Direction (Basal) **Fracture:** Irregular/Uneven **Hardness:** 6 to 7 on Mohs Hardness Scale **Streak:** Colorless to gray **Luster:** Glassy **Density:** 3.43 g/cm^3 **Locations:** United States, Italy, Austria, Norway, Canada, France, Australia **Uses:** Gemstones, Collections **Features:** Epidote is most commonly found in metamorphic rocks and can be the altered form of plagioclase feldspar. Often forms beautiful crystal shapes that may have striations (lines) on the crystal faces.
FLUORITE - MINERAL	**Color:** Blue, Red, Purple, Yellow, Green or White **Crystal Shape:** Cubes, Octahedrons, Dodecahedrons. Sometime twinned. **Cleavage:** Octahedral **Fracture:** Conchoidal to splintery **Hardness:** 4 on Mohs Hardness Scale **Streak:** White **Luster:** Glassy **Density:** 3.181 g/cm^3 **Locations:** Germany, Italy, Switzerland, England, Mexico, Canada, United States **Uses:** Enamels, Cooking Utensils, Telescopes, Camera Lenses **Features:** Often found in rock veins.

GALENA - MINERAL	**Color:** Dark gray, Silver **Crystal Shape:** Cube, sometimes forms granular masses. **Cleavage:** Cubic **Fracture:** Conchoidal **Hardness:** 2.5 to 2.8 on Mohs Hardness Scale **Streak:** Dark gray **Luster:** Metallic **Density:** 7.57 g/cm^3 **Locations:** United States, Australia, Mexico, West Germany and Italy. Some of the best known deposits are from Joplin, Missouri. **Uses:** Used for its lead content. **Features:** Heavy with shiny surfaces.
GARNET - MINERAL	**Color:** Red, Orange, Yellow, Green, Blue, Purple, Brown, Black, Pink and Colorless **Crystal Shape:** Dodecahedral or Trapezohedral **Cleavage:** None **Fracture:** Conchoidal **Hardness:** 6.5 to 7.5 on Mohs Hardness Scale **Streak:** White **Luster:** Glassy to Resinous **Density:** 3.58 – 4.32 g/cm^3 **Locations:** Worldwide **Uses:** Jewelry and Abrasives **Features:** Garnet forms in 16 varieties with many colors and are considered a group of minerals. Typically forms in metamorphic rocks. Common in schist and gneiss rocks as minor mineral. Blue garnet is the rarest.
GYPSUM - MINERAL	**Color:** Colorless or White **Crystal Shape:** Tabular. Often forms twins or rosettes. **Cleavage:** 3 Directions (one perfect direction) **Fracture:** Conchoidal to splintery **Hardness:** 2 on Mohs Hardness Scale **Streak:** White **Luster:** Pearly to Glassy **Density:** 2.308 g/cm^3 **Locations:** Mexico, Italy, Russia, France, Canada and United States **Uses:** Paints, Tile, Drywall, Blackboard Chalk, Fertilizer, Plaster of Paris **Features:** Formed from water evaporation when lakes or oceans dry. Gypsum will dissolved over time in water. Selenite is a fibrous form of gypsum.
HALITE - MINERAL	**Color:** Colorless, White, Yellow, Red, Brown, Light Blue, Dark Blue, Violet, Pink **Crystal Shape:** Cube **Cleavage:** Cubic **Fracture:** Conchoidal **Hardness:** 2.5 on Mohs Hardness Scale **Streak:** White **Luster:** Glassy **Density:** 2.165 g/cm^3 **Locations:** Germany, Poland, Spain, Austria, United States, Italy **Uses:** Salt for food preparation and in the chemical industry **Features:** Evaporite mineral. All salt comes from the seas. Halite is formed when seas or lakes dry and can be found in wide, thick layers.

HEMATITE - MINERAL	**Color:** Gray to Black **Crystal Shape:** Rhombohedrons. Stubby Crystals, Rosettes and Granular Masses. **Cleavage:** None **Fracture:** Irregular / Conchoidal **Hardness:** 5 - 6 on Mohs Hardness Scale **Streak:** Red-brown to dark cherry red **Luster:** Metallic to earthy **Density:** 5.255 g/cm^3 **Locations:** Worldwide **Uses:** Jewelry, plate-glass, mined for its iron content, red pigments. **Features:** If present in rock, will cause the rock to be colored reddish. Heavy mineral.
HORNBLENDE - MINERAL	**Color:** Dark Green, Brown to Black **Crystal Shape:** Prismatic, Stubby Crystals **Cleavage:** Prismatic at 120° **Fracture:** Uneven to conchoidal **Hardness:** 5 to 6 on Mohs Hardness Scale **Streak:** Colorless **Luster:** Glassy **Density:** 3.0- 3.4 g/cm^3 **Locations:** Worldwide **Uses:** Collecting **Features:** Heavy, translucent along edges. The cleavage directions allow hornblende to have a diamond shaped appearance viewed from the side.
JASPER - | MINERAL	**Color:** Red, Yellow, Brown, Black, Gray or White **Crystal Shape:** None. May form aggregates and nodules. **Cleavage:** None **Fracture:** Conchoidal **Hardness:** 7 on Mohs Hardness Scale **Streak:** White **Luster:** Glassy **Density:** 2.6 g/cm^3 **Locations:** United States **Uses:** Home decorations, jewelry **Features:** Microcrystalline form of quartz that forms inside the cracks of other rocks. Jasper is common in sedimentary rocks and may often contain iron oxides.

KYANITE - MINERAL	**Color:** Light Blue, Blue-Gray or Black **Crystal Shape:** Long, blade shape **Cleavage:** 1 Direction (Basal) **Fracture:** Splintery **Hardness:** 4 to 5 along blades and 6 to 7 across the blades on Mohs Hardness Scale **Streak:** White **Luster:** Glassy to Pearly **Density:** 3.67 g/cm^3 **Locations:** Switzerland, Italy, Austria, France, Kenya, Brazil, United States **Uses:** Ceramic Products like porcelain plumbing fixtures and dinnerware, Electrical Insulators, Abrasives **Features:** Usually found in metamorphic schist and gneiss rocks. Crystals are long and blade-like. Hardness varies by direction on mineral which is a good indicator of the mineral.
LEPIDOLITE MICA - MINERAL	**Color:** Purple. Sometimes Colorless, Yellow or Gray. **Crystal Shape:** Thin sheets called "books" **Cleavage:** Perfect Basal (Platy) **Fracture:** None due to elasticity of crystal sheets **Hardness:** 2.5 to 4 on Mohs Hardness Scale **Streak:** Colorless **Luster:** Glassy to Pearly **Density:** 2.83 g/cm^3 **Locations:** United States, Brazil, Madagascar, Australia, Germany, Canada, Japan **Uses:** Lepidolite is a source of lithium which has many uses including medicine and atomic energy. **Features:** Mica mineral found mostly in pegmatite rocks. Forms as a "book" with super thin crystal pages. Your fingernail can be used to flake apart the individual layers of the book. The lithium in the mineral causes the purple color.
LIMONITE - MINERAL	**Color:** Yellow-Brown **Crystal Shape:** None **Cleavage:** None **Fracture:** None **Hardness:** 5 to 5.5 on Mohs Hardness Scale **Streak:** Yellow-Brown **Luster:** Earthy **Density:** 2.7 – 4.3 g/cm^3 **Locations:** United States **Uses:** Used for dyes and pigments **Features:** Limonite does not form distinct crystal shapes. Limonite is a generic name for iron hydroxide minerals; therefore, there is no set chemical formula.

MAGNETITE - MINERAL	**Color:** Black **Crystal Shape:** Octahedrons and Dodecahedrons **Cleavage:** None **Fracture:** Irregular / Uneven **Hardness:** 5.5 to 6.5 on Mohs Hardness Scale **Streak:** Black **Luster:** Metallic **Density:** 5.2 g/cm^3 **Locations:** Sweden, Austria, United States, Italy, Switzerland, South Africa, Russia **Uses:** Used mainly for its iron content. **Features:** Heavy. Can be picked up by a magnet. Can be found in most igneous and metamorphic rocks and many sedimentary rocks. Crystal faces may exhibit striations (lines) on the surface.
MALACHITE - MINERAL	**Color:** Green **Crystal Shape:** Fibrous, Aggregates or Films on copper minerals. Rarely forms crystals. **Cleavage:** 1 Direction (Basal) **Fracture:** Conchoidal / Irregular **Hardness:** 3.5 to 4 on Mohs Hardness Scale **Streak:** Light Green **Luster:** Glassy to Silky **Density:** 4.0 g/cm^3 **Locations:** United States, Africa, Russia, South America, Australia, Germany, France, among others **Uses:** Jewelry, Building Materials and Ornamental Stone **Features:** Often found in association with copper deposits and the mineral azurite.
MICROCLINE - MINERAL	**Color:** Pink, green, blue-green, white, red or yellow. **Crystal Shape:** Prismatic – short, Tabular, often twinned **Cleavage:** 2 Directions at almost 90° **Fracture:** Irregular / Uneven **Hardness:** 6 to 6.5 on Mohs Hardness Scale **Streak:** White **Luster:** Glassy **Density:** 2.56 g/cm^3 **Locations:** Worldwide **Uses:** Glazes, enamels, ornamental, jewelry, collections **Features:** One of the feldspar minerals that occur in igneous and metamorphic rocks. Over time, microcline will decay into clay. Microcline has almost 90 degree cleavage and may have lines on a flat side that look like scratches.

MILKY QUARTZ - MINERAL	**Color:** White **Crystal Shape:** Hexagonal prismatic crystal (6-sided barrel) with a hexagonal pyramid on each end **Cleavage:** None **Fracture:** Conchoidal **Hardness:** 7 on Mohs Hardness Scale **Streak:** White **Luster:** Glassy **Density:** 2.66 g/cm^3 **Locations:** Milky Quartz very common in the Alps. Quartz is the most common, widespread mineral on Earth. **Uses:** Quartz has many industrial uses - prisms, lenses and gauges, Glass, Paints and Abrasives. **Features:** Milky quartz is the most common variety of quartz. Occurs in hydrothermal veins and pegmatites but is common in all rock types. The white color is caused by many bubbles of gas and liquid in the crystal.
MUSCOVITE MICA - MINERAL	**Color:** Gray, Silver, White, Brown, Rose or Green **Crystal Shape:** Thin sheets called "books" **Cleavage:** 1 Direction (Basal) **Fracture:** None due to elasticity of crystal sheets **Hardness:** 2 to 2.5 on Mohs Hardness Scale **Streak:** Colorless **Luster:** Glassy **Density:** 2.83 g/cm^3 **Locations:** United States, Canada, Switzerland, India, Italy, Austria **Uses:** Insulation and porcelain **Features:** One of the most common minerals in rocks. Forms as a "book" with super thin crystal pages. Your fingernail can be used to flake apart the individual layers of the book.
OLIVINE - MINERAL	**Color:** Olive-Green to Yellowish **Crystal Shape:** Prismatic, Stubby Crystals, Granular Masses **Cleavage:** 2 Directions **Fracture:** Conchoidal **Hardness:** 6.5 to 7 on Mohs Hardness Scale **Streak:** White **Luster:** Glassy **Density:** 3.271 g/cm^3 **Locations:** Egypt, Norway, Germany, United States, Italy **Uses:** Clear variety is used to make jewelry as the gemstone Peridot. **Features:** One of the most common minerals on Earth. Occurs in both igneous and metamorphic rocks.

OPAL - MINERAL	**Color:** Colorless, Pink, Yellow, Red, Green, Brown, Milky White, Light Blue or Black **Crystal Shape:** None. Never forms crystals. **Cleavage:** None **Fracture:** Conchoidal to splintery **Hardness:** 5.5 to 6.5 on Mohs Hardness Scale **Streak:** White **Luster:** Greasy, waxy, glassy or dull **Density:** 1.9 – 2.3 g/cm^3 **Locations:** Worldwide **Uses:** Jewelry, Abrasives, Insulators and Porcelain **Features:** Opal is a water-rich silicate. Forms in small veins, crusts or globules. Fluorescent yellow or green in ultraviolet light.
PYRITE - MINERAL	**Color:** Yellow, Goldish-Yellow **Crystal Shape:** Cube, Octahedron, Pyritohedral. May form twins. **Cleavage:** None **Fracture:** Conchoidal **Hardness:** 6 to 6 ½ on Mohs Hardness Scale **Streak:** Greenish-Brown to Black **Luster:** Metallic **Density:** 5.01 g/cm^3 **Locations:** Worldwide **Uses:** Used in the production of sulfuric acid. **Features:** Known as "fools gold" but it is lighter and harder than gold. Pyrite crystals may have striations (lines) on faces. Will give off a spark if hit with a hammer.
QUARTZ CRYSTAL - MINERAL	**Color:** Colorless **Crystal Shape:** Hexagonal prismatic crystal (6-sided barrel) with a hexagonal pyramid on each end **Cleavage:** None **Fracture:** Conchoidal **Hardness:** 7 on Mohs Hardness Scale **Streak:** White **Luster:** Glassy **Density:** 2.66 g/cm^3 **Locations:** Worldwide **Uses:** Quartz has many industrial uses - prisms, lenses and gauges, Glass, Paints and Abrasives. **Features:** Quartz crystals mainly form in pegmatites, Alpine fissures and in geodes.

RHODONITE - MINERAL	**Color:** Pink (rosy-red) **Crystal Shape:** Granular masses, rare tabular crystals **Cleavage:** Prismatic - almost 90° **Fracture:** Conchoidal, Irregular **Hardness:** 5.5 to 6.5 on Mohs Hardness Scale **Streak:** White **Luster:** Glassy **Density:** 3.726 g/cm^3 **Locations:** United States, Australia, Brazil, Russia, Canada, Sweden, England **Uses:** Gemstones for jewelry **Features:** Found in metamorphic rocks and typically has black mineral veins running through the pink grains. Rhodonite often has a brown color due to oxidation on the mineral surface.
SERPENTINE - MINERAL	**Color:** Light Green, Yellowish Green, Creamy White, Black **Crystal Shape:** Massive, Fibrous **Cleavage:** 1 Direction (Basal) **Fracture:** Conchoidal, Splintery **Hardness:** 2.5 to 4 on Mohs Hardness Scale **Streak:** White **Luster:** Greasy, waxy, or silky depending on variety **Density:** 2.5 – 2.6 g/cm^3 **Locations:** Italy, United States of America **Uses:** Sometimes used in buildings as polished slabs for facing, insulation. **Features:** Serpentine occurs in low grade metamorphic rocks. The fibrous form of serpentine is chrysotile asbestos.
SODALITE - MINERAL	**Color:** Royal Blue, White or Gray with Green Tints **Crystal Shape:** Forms as a mass, rarely dodecahedral crystals. **Cleavage:** 1 Direction(Basal), poor **Fracture:** Conchoidal **Hardness:** 5.5 to 6 on Mohs Hardness Scale **Streak:** White **Luster:** Glassy **Density:** 2.31 g/cm^3 **Locations:** Canada, United States, South America, Portugal, Romania, Burma, Russia **Uses:** Jewelry, Polished Slabs and Carved Ornaments **Features:** Not a common mineral but forms typically in igneous rocks.
STAUROLITE - MINERAL	**Color:** Reddish Brown to Black **Crystal Shape:** Prismatic, often forms twins in shape of a cross **Cleavage:** 1 Direction (Basal) **Fracture:** Conchoidal **Hardness:** 7 to 7.5 on Mohs Hardness Scale **Streak:** Colorless **Luster:** Glassy to Resinous **Density:** 3.686 g/cm^3 **Locations:** Switzerland, Bavaria, Scotland, United States **Uses:** Jewelry. **Features:** Geologists use the presence of staurolite to determine the metamorphic grade of the rock. Very hard, stable and insoluble.

SULFUR - MINERAL	**Color:** Yellow to Yellowish-Brown **Crystal Shape:** Dipyramidal Crystals, Granular Aggregates **Cleavage:** None **Fracture:** Conchoidal, Irregular **Hardness:** 1.5 to 2.5 on Mohs Hardness Scale **Streak:** White **Luster:** Greasy **Density:** 2.076 g/cm^3 **Locations:** United States, Italy, Sicily, Switzerland, France, Mexico **Uses:** Explosives, dyes, sulfuric acids, insecticides **Features:** Sulfur will dissolve in warm water and crack when exposed to heat. Sulfur has a mild smell of rotten-eggs and the smell gets stronger as the mineral warms. The rotten egg smell is noticeable during a streak test.
TALC - MINERAL	**Color:** White, Greenish-White, Bluish-Green, Gray or Brown **Crystal Shape:** Aggregates, never crystals **Cleavage:** 1 Direction (Basal) if in crystal form **Fracture:** Fibrous **Hardness:** 1 on Mohs Hardness Scale **Streak:** White **Luster:** Pearly, Greasy, Waxy **Density:** 2.78 g/cm^3 **Locations:** Austria, India, Italy, United States, Russia, Australia & others **Uses:** Paper and rubber production, cosmetics, paint and textiles **Features:** Feels greasy. Thin sections of talc may be flexible. Occurs in igneous and metamorphic rocks.
TOURMALINE - MINERAL	**Color:** Black, Green, Brown, Red, Blue, Yellow or Pink **Crystal Shape:** Prismatic – elongated, hexagonal or triangular in cross-section. Crystals may have striations (lines) on faces. **Cleavage:** None **Fracture:** Conchoidal **Hardness:** 7 on Mohs Hardness Scale **Streak:** Colorless **Luster:** Glassy to Pearly **Density:** 2.9 – 3.1 g/cm^3 **Locations:** United States, Brazil, Italy, Russia **Uses:** Gemstones, High-Pressure Gauges **Features:** Tourmaline is a member of a family of six different minerals. Tourmaline, which often occurs in igneous rocks, does not degrade and therefore, is often found in gravel or other sedimentary rocks.
ULEXITE – MINERAL	**Color:** Colorless, White, Gray **Crystal Shape:** Rounded Masses, rarely forms crystals **Cleavage:** None **Fracture:** Irregular / Uneven **Hardness:** 2 to 2.5 on Mohs Hardness Scale **Streak:** White **Luster:** Silky **Density:** 1.955 g/cm^3 **Locations:** California & Nevada, United States, Chile **Features:** Fiber optic mineral. Called "TV Stone" for its ability to transmit images through its fibers from the bottom to the top of the mineral when polished on both sides. Ulexite is soluble in hot water.

Common Igneous Rock Information

ANDESITE – IGNEOUS ROCK	**Color:** Light to Dark Gray, Brown to Black, Reddish-Pink, Green **Type:** Extrusive or Intrusive **Minerals:** *Majors:* Feldspar, Biotite *Minors:* amphibolite, pyroxenes **Texture:** Porphyritic **Locations:** Japan, South America, Caribbean, Mexico **Uses:** Building materials **Features:** Often found with volcanic ash or tuff.
ANORTHOSITE – IGNEOUS ROCK	**Color:** White to Light Gray **Type:** Intrusive **Minerals:** *Major:* Feldspar *Minors:* Pyroxene, Olivine, Magnetite, Illmenite, Chromite and Garnet **Texture:** Coarse-grained **Locations:** Canada, Norway, United States **Uses:** Ornamental building stone **Features:** May display iridescence.
BASALT – IGNEOUS ROCK	**Color:** Dark Gray to Greenish to Black **Type:** Extrusive **Minerals:** *Majors:* Pyroxene and Feldspar *Minors:* Olivine, Magnetite, Hematite, Quartz and others **Texture:** Fine-grained **Locations:** India, United States, Scotland, Iceland, Greenland, Brazil **Uses:** Road paving, Crushed stone for roads and railroads, Building Stone, Fiber Glass **Features:** Heavy. Basalt is the most common extrusive igneous rock in the world.
CARBONATITE – IGNEOUS ROCK	**Color:** Light Gray or Yellowish **Type:** Intrusive and Extrusive **Minerals:** *Majors:* Calcite or Dolomite *Minors:* Olivine, Magnetite, Fluorite **Texture:** Fine to Medium-grained **Locations:** South Africa, Sweden, Norway, Russia, Canada, United States, France **Uses:** Used as a source for its minor minerals **Features:** May be confused with marble.
DIORITE – IGNEOUS ROCK	**Color:** Gray to Blackish-Gray to Dark Green **Type:** Intrusive **Minerals:** *Majors:* Feldspar and Hornblende *Minors:* Magnetite, Quartz, Mica, Pyroxenes (such as augite) **Texture:** Medium to Coarse-grained **Locations:** France, Italy, Germany, Romania, Finland, Sweden and United States **Uses:** Building stone and Polished slabs **Features:** Common near subduction plate boundaries.

GABBRO – IGNEOUS ROCK	**Color:** Dark Gray **Type:** Intrusive **Minerals:** *Majors:* Feldspar and Pyroxene *Minors:* Olivine, Magnetite, Amphibole, Chromite. **Texture:** Medium to Coarse-grained **Locations:** Switzerland, Italy, United States, Scotland, Greece and Turkey **Uses:** Gabbro is typically fragile which limits it uses. May be used for its minor mineral content. **Features:** Gabbro can change color based on which minor minerals are present.
GRANITE – IGNEOUS ROCK	**Color:** White, Light Gray, Pink, Red, Yellowish **Type:** Intrusive **Minerals:** *Majors:* Feldspar, Quartz, Mica *Minors:* Hornblende, Magnetite, Garnet, Pyroxene **Texture:** Medium-grained. Crystals are all similar in size. **Locations:** Most common rock on Earth's surface - can be found in most countries. **Uses:** Building materials and Monuments **Features:** Hard and tough rock. Granite color varies based on minerals present.
GRAPHIC GRANITE – IGNEOUS ROCK	**Color:** White, Tan Or Pink Feldspar with Smoky, White or Colorless Quartz **Type:** Intrusive **Minerals:** Feldspar and Quartz **Texture:** Coarse-grained **Locations:** Worldwide although graphic granite is one of the more rare forms of granite. **Uses:** Ornamental, Collecting **Features:** Quartz forms in parallel, rod shapes in a feldspar matrix. The quartz looks like script characters when cut perpendicular to their growth. The name graphic granite comes from the Latin word "Graphus" which means 'to write.'
MONZONITE – IGNEOUS ROCK	**Color:** Dark Gray, Green, Red **Type:** Intrusive **Minerals:** *Majors:* Feldspars, Pyroxene, Hornblende *Minors:* Magnetite, Quartz, Mica, Olivine **Texture:** Medium-grained **Locations:** Norway, United States, Scotland **Uses:** Building stone **Features:** Common rock in rift or tectonic zones.
OBSIDIAN – IGNEOUS ROCK	**Color:** Black; however, if a piece is very thin it can be light and transparent. **Type:** Extrusive **Minerals:** *Majors:* Feldspar, Quartz, Mica *Minors:* Hornblende, Magnetite, Garnet, Pyroxene **Texture:** Glass **Locations:** Yellowstone National Park (United States), Hungary, Japan and Italy. **Uses:** Used in industry to make rock wool. **Features:** Obsidian is made of same major minerals as granite, rhyolite and pumice but looks different because the rock is formed by a different method. Obsidian is formed when the lava cools very, very quickly and becomes glass-like.

PEGMATITE – IGNEOUS ROCK	**Color:** Light color that varies with crystal content. **Type:** Intrusive **Minerals:** *Majors:* Quartz, Mica, and Feldspar *Minors:* Garnet, Topaz, Beryl, Ruby, Pyrite, Fluorite, Emerald, and many more **Texture:** Coarse-grained. **Locations:** United States, Brazil, Russia **Uses:** Mined for its mineral content. **Features:** Large crystals are characteristic of this rock. The large crystals are formed when the rock cools very, very slowly.
PERIDOTITE – IGNEOUS ROCK	**Color:** Black or light to dark green also **Type:** Intrusive **Minerals:** *Majors:* Olivine and Pyroxene *Minors:* Mica and Hornblende **Texture:** Medium-grained **Locations:** South Africa, United States, Canada, Russia, England **Uses:** South African diamond deposits occur in peridotites. Peridotite is often found with minerals containing nickel and is mined for the nickel content. **Features:** May be made almost exclusively of olivine. Often found with nickel-bearing minerals.
PUMICE – IGNEOUS ROCK	**Color:** Light Gray, Yellowish, Red, Tan **Type:** Extrusive **Minerals:** *Majors:* Feldspar, Quartz, Mica **Texture:** Vesicular (the rock has many holes or openings) **Locations:** Italy and, Indonesia **Uses:** Abrasives and Insulation **Features:** Pumice is made of same major minerals as granite, rhyolite and obsidian but looks different because the rock is formed by a different method. Pumice is formed when the molten lava was thrown in the air and becomes frothy and sponge-like and then cools. Pumice is so light weight it floats on water.
RHYOLITE – IGNEOUS ROCK	**Color:** Light Pink to Gray **Type:** Extrusive **Minerals:** *Majors:* Feldspar, Quartz, Mica *Minors:* Hornblende, Magnetite, Garnet, Pyroxene **Texture:** Fine-grained with some larger grains visible **Locations:** Italy, United States, England, Hungary, Romania, Africa, Japan **Uses:** Thermal insulation **Features:** Rhyolite is made of same major minerals as granite, pumice and obsidian but looks different because the rock cools at a different speed. The fine-grained texture is formed from fast cooling of the lava. However, the lava cools slower than it does during the formation of obsidian.
SCORIA – IGNEOUS ROCK	**Color:** Red, brown, or black **Type:** Extrusive **Minerals:** Can vary (mostly feldspar, pyroxene, and biotite) **Texture:** Vesicular **Locations:** United States, Canada, Easter Island, New Zealand **Uses:** Often used in landscaping beds and is called "lava rock," road beds **Features:** Forms during a volcanic eruption often as a hard crust on the top of the lava. Air escaping from the magma/lava causes the holes in the rock.

SNOWFLAKE OBSIDIAN – IGNEOUS ROCK	**Color:** Black with White "Snowflakes" **Type:** Extrusive **Minerals:** *Majors:* Feldspar, Quartz, Mica *Minors:* Hornblende, Magnetite, Garnet, Pyroxene **Texture:** Glassy **Locations:** Yellowstone National Park (United States), Hungary, Japan and Italy. **Uses:** Used in industry to make rock wool. **Features:** Obsidian is formed when the lava cools very, very quickly and becomes glass-like. The snowflakes are actually small white crystals that are shaped like needles and form in a circle as the rocks breaks down over time. This process is called devitrification and the white spots are actually the mineral cristobalite, which is a form of quartz.
SYENITE – IGNEOUS ROCK	**Color:** Gray, Pink or Violet **Type:** Intrusive **Minerals:** *Majors:* Feldspars and Hornblende *Minors:* Pyroxene, Mica, Quartz, Magnetite **Texture:** Fine to Medium-grained **Locations:** Egypt, Italy, Germany, Norway, United States **Uses:** Polished slab for buildings
TRACHYTE – IGNEOUS ROCK	**Color:** White, Light Gray, Light Brown or Green **Type:** Extrusive **Minerals:** *Majors:* Feldspar and Biotite mica *Minors:* Amphibole, Pyroxene, Magnetite, Garnet and others **Texture:** Porphyritic – generally fine-grained with large crystals visible **Locations:** Tahiti, Africa, Germany, Italy **Uses:** Paving and Building materials (such as flooring) **Features:** The fine-grained crystals are very small, long feldspar crystals. The long crystal shape can be seen under a microscope.
VOLCANIC ASH – IGNEOUS MATERIAL	**Color:** Gray **Type:** Extrusive **Composition:** Bits of rock and volcanic glass **Texture:** Fine to medium – clay to sand sized particles **Locations:** Deposits after some volcanic eruptions **Features:** Steam buildup in a volcano causes violent eruptions that shred the surrounding rock into small, ash particles.
VOLCANIC BRECCIA – IGNEOUS ROCK	**Color:** Grayish, Greenish **Type:** Extrusive **Minerals:** Various **Texture:** Angular, coarse grains with fine grained background rock **Locations:** Limited to volcanic areas **Uses:** Limited use, possible as building materials **Features:** Volcanic breccia is typically formed during an eruption when rock fragments are plucked off of the inside of a volcano and are stuck in the lava or when fragments are picked up by flowing lava. The major difference is a breccia and a conglomerate is that the rock fragments in a breccia are angular and the rock fragments in a conglomerate are rounded.

Common Sedimentary Rock Information

ARKOSE – SEDIMENTARY ROCK	**Color:** Gray, Pink, Red **How it Forms:** Arkose is formed when igneous rocks break apart and the pieces travel to a river, lake or ocean. These pieces are glued (cemented) together with quartz, calcite or similar mineral. **Minerals:** *Major:* Feldspar *Minors:* Quartz and Mica **Texture:** Coarse-grained **Locations:** Worldwide **Uses:** Building materials **Features:** No fossils present.
BITUMINOUS COAL – SEDIMENTARY ROCK	**Color:** Black **How it Forms:** Coal is made from plants. **Minerals/Content:** *Major:* Carbon from plant material *Minors:* Pyrite and Quartz. **Texture:** Scaly and compact **Locations:** North America, England, France, Belgium, Germany, China, Siberia, Australia **Uses:** Used by many industrial facilities for fuel. **Features:** Shiny. Coal typically forms in lagoons and basins when the plant material loses water and the carbon content of the coal increases.
CHERT – SEDIMENTARY ROCK	**Color:** Gray or White. Light hues of Red, Yellow and Brown. **How it Forms:** Cryptocrystalline form of quartz that forms as nodules and layers in other sedimentary rocks such as dolomite, limestone and chalk. **Texture:** Cryptocrystalline **Locations:** Worldwide. Nice specimens found in Dover, England. **Uses:** Firearms, prehistoric arrowheads and tools, headstones **Features:** Chert is technically a sedimentary rock but is often referred to a mineral. May contain fossils. Will spark when struck.
CONGLOMERATE – SEDIMENTARY ROCK	**Color:** Varies based on what minerals are present. **How it Forms:** Conglomerate is formed in an ocean or river setting when pebbles are glued together with smaller particles of sand and clay. **Minerals:** Can contain any type of rock fragments. **Texture:** Very Coarse-grained pebbles with fine-grained silt and sand. **Locations:** Worldwide **Uses:** Building materials **Features:** Can be confused with breccia. However, breccia has angular fragments and conglomerate has rounded fragments.
COQUINA – SEDIMENTARY ROCK	**Color:** Tan **How it Forms:** Coquina is formed in ocean settings and marine reefs when pieces of shells and coral are glued together with calcite. **Minerals/Content:** *Majors:* Shells and Coral *Minor:* Calcite **Texture:** Rough – shell pieces **Locations:** Worldwide **Uses:** Building materials. Some coquina which contains phosphate has been mined for fertilizer. Features: Coquina has jagged edges that can be sharp. This rock is often called a limestone. Due to its calcite content, will react with acid.

FOSSILIFEROUS LIMESTONE – SEDIMENTARY ROCK	**Color:** White, pink, red, gray or black **How it Forms:** Limestone forms in the ocean from calcite deposits. **Minerals:** *Major:* Calcite *Minors:* fossils, various minerals **Texture:** Fine-grained with fossil fragments & impressions **Locations:** Worldwide **Uses:** Building stones **Features:** Limestone is great for preserving fossils of ancient animals and plants. Limestone will react with acid.
LIGNITE COAL – SEDIMENTARY ROCK	**Color:** Brownish - Black **How it Forms:** Organic carbon from plant material, i.e. peat. Lignite is formed when peat is squeezed under high pressure but not high temperatures. **Texture:** No crystals **Locations:** United States, Germany, England, Turkey, France, Russia **Uses:** Jewelry as gemstone "Jet" and fuel **Features:** Lignite coal is the lowest grade of coal.
LIMESTONE – SEDIMENTARY ROCK	**Color:** White, Pink, Red, Gray or Black **How it Forms:** Limestone form in the ocean from calcite deposits. **Minerals:** *Major:* Calcite *Minors:* various **Texture:** Fine-grained **Locations:** Worldwide **Uses:** Building stones. **Features:** Limestone is great for preserving fossils of ancient animals and plants. Limestone will react with acid.
LOESS – SEDIMENTARY ROCK	**Color:** Tan, Pink, Gray, Yellow, or Brown **How it Forms:** Loess is formed from windblown sediment in glacier or desert areas. **Minerals:** *Major:* Quartz *Minors:* Feldspar, Calcite, Dolomite, Clay minerals **Texture:** Very fine-grained **Locations:** Russia, United States, China, Hungary, Belgium **Uses:** None. **Features:** Loess is very fragile and will break apart when touched.
OOLITIC LIMESTONE – SEDIMENTARY ROCK	**Color:** White, Pink, Red, Gray or Black **How it Forms:** Limestone forms in the ocean from calcite deposits. **Minerals:** *Major:* Calcite *Minors:* various **Texture:** Fine-grained with calcite oolites **Locations:** Worldwide **Uses:** Building stones **Features:** Oolites are small, rounded particles that often form as layers of calcite deposited around a single sand grain. Limestone will react with acid.
SANDSTONE – SEDIMENTARY ROCK	**Color:** White, Yellowish or other colors based on minerals present. *Example:* Red Sandstones are red due to iron oxide bands in the rock. **How it Forms:** Sand-sized (beach sand) particles are stacked in a river, lake, ocean or desert and glued together with quartz or calcite. **Minerals:** *Majors:* Quartz, Feldspar *Minor:* Calcite **Texture:** Medium-grained **Locations:** Worldwide **Uses:** Building materials and industrial processing **Features:** The spaces between sand grains can be either open or filled. Sandstones make good places for water and oil to be stored below the land surface.

SEDIMENTARY BRECCIA – SEDIMENTARY ROCK	**Color:** Reddish-Brown. Can vary depending on the rock fragments present. **How it Forms:** Forms where rock fragments are created such as landsides, moving glaciers, and cave-ins. **Minerals:** Can contain any type of rock fragments. **Texture:** Coarse-grained. Angular fragments in fine-grained rock. **Locations:** United State, England, Wales **Uses:** Building materials **Features:** Can be confused with conglomerate. However, breccia has angular fragments and conglomerate has rounded fragments.
SHALE – SEDIMENTARY ROCK	**Color:** Gray, Red **How it Forms:** Shale typically forms in slow moving water such as lakes and the deep ocean which allows the clays to fall to the bottom and form layers. The clay layers harden over time into rock. **Minerals:** *Majors:* Clay minerals *Minors:* Quartz, Feldspar, Calcite or Dolomite **Texture:** Very fine grained **Locations:** Worldwide. **Uses:** Tile, Brick, Pottery, Portland Cement **Features:** More than half of all sedimentary rocks on Earth are believed to be shale. Shale can be split into layers. May contain fossils.
SILTSTONE – SEDIMENTARY ROCK	**Color:** Tan or Gray **How it Forms:** Siltstone usually forms offshore, in quiet environments. **Minerals:** Quartz and Feldspar **Texture:** Fine-grained (smaller grains than sandstone but larger grains than shale) Grains are hard to see but you can feel them. **Locations:** Worldwide, although not as common as sandstone or shale. **Uses:** Collecting **Features:** Cannot be easily split into thin layers like shale. Siltstones typically only form very thin layers. Hard, durable, and can contain fossils.

Common Metamorphic Rock Information

AMPHIBOLITE – METAMORPHIC ROCK	**Color:** Dark Green often speckled with white and yellow **Original Rock Type:** Gabbro or Basalt lava **Minerals:** *Majors:* Amphibole and Feldspar *Minors:* Magnetite, Quartz, Mica, Garnet **Texture:** Medium to Coarse-grained **Locations:** Germany, France, England, Norway, Brazil and North America **Uses:** Sometimes located near copper deposits and mined for the copper content. **Features:** Usually a regional metamorphic rock. Often found near copper deposits.
ANTHRACITE COAL - METAMORPHIC ROCK	**Color:** Black **Original Material:** Organic carbon from plant material. Anthracite has the highest carbon content of all coal varieties. **Texture:** No crystal structure. **Locations:** United States, England, Canada, Peru **Uses:** Fuel. Anthracite coal gives off the most heat of all coal varieties. **Features:** Hard, brittle and almost metallic in appearance. Anthracite is the rarest and most expensive form of coal.

GARNET SCHIST - METAMORPHIC ROCK	**Color:** Gray, Silvery or Brown **Original Rock Type:** Clayey rocks with some calcite content such as siltstone or mudstone **Minerals:** *Majors:* Quartz and Mica *Minors:* Garnet and others **Texture:** Typically fine-grained with visible garnet crystals included. **Locations:** Worldwide **Uses:** Garnets crystals are often used for jewelry. Limited use a building materials. **Features:** Garnet schist is named for the abundance of garnet minerals in the rock. Fine grains of mica give the rock a silky and shiny appearance. If broken, schist will break into wavy surfaces.
GNEISS – METAMORPHIC ROCK	**Color:** Light Gray and White **Original Rock Type:** Granite, Arkose, Siltstones or Sandstones **Minerals:** *Majors:* Feldspar and Mica *Minors:* many **Texture:** Medium to Coarse-grained **Locations:** France, United States, Germany, Spain, Portugal, Japan **Uses:** Building materials such as rough stones and polished slabs **Features:** Pronounced "Nice." Gneiss often appears to have bands of black and white minerals that are formed when the rock is heated and squeezed.
GRANITOID GNEISS – METAMORPHIC ROCK	**Color:** Light Gray and White **Original Rock Type:** Granite, Arkose, Siltstones or Sandstones **Minerals:** *Majors:* Feldspar and Mica *Minors:* many **Texture:** Medium to Coarse-grained **Locations:** France, United States, Germany, Spain, Portugal, Japan, Alps **Uses:** Building materials such as rough stones and polished slabs **Features:** Pronounced "Nice." Gneiss often appears to have bands of black and white minerals that are formed when the rock is heated and squeezed. Granitoid Gneiss may look similar to the original granite rock.
HORNFELS – METAMORPHIC ROCK	**Color:** Ranges from dark to light depending on the type of original rock **Original Rock Type:** Sandstone, Clay or Shale, Limestone, Diabase. **Minerals:** *Majors:* Quartz, Feldspar, Mica *Minors:* many **Texture:** Fine-grained **Locations:** France, Norway, United States and Germany **Uses:** Collecting **Features:** Hornfels forms around the edges of instrusive igneous rocks. Hornfels is formed through heating the rock with little to no pressure.
MARBLE – METAMORPHIC ROCK	**Color:** White, Yellow, Brown, Green or Black **Original Rock Type:** Limestone. **Minerals:** *Major:* Calcite *Minors:* Dolomite, Quartz, Mica, Pyroxene, Olivine, Talc and others **Texture:** Fine to Very Coarse-grained **Locations:** Italy and United States **Uses:** Building materials such as rough stone and polished slabs. Used for sculpture. **Features:** Very hard and tough.

PHYLLITE – METAMORPHIC ROCK	**Color:** Light Gray, Silver Gray or Greenish **Original Rock Type:** Sedimentary rocks **Minerals:** *Majors:* Quartz, Mica, Chlorite *Minors:* Feldspar, Tourmaline, Pyrite, Garnet, Calcite and others **Texture:** Very Fine-grained **Locations:** United States, Austria, Germany, Belgium, England **Uses:** Limited use as building materials **Features:** Rock may have a wavy appearance.
QUARTZITE – METAMORPHIC ROCK	**Color:** White, Pink. Can have other colors if minerals other than quartz are present. **Original Rock Type:** metamorphic form of sedimentary rocks such as or-thoquartzite, greywacke, arkose, siltstones **Minerals:** *Majors:* Quartz *Majors:* Mica, Feldspar, Magnetite, Garnet, Calcite &others **Texture:** Fine to medium grained. Granular texture. **Locations:** United States, India, Brazil **Uses:** Building materials, glass and ceramic industry **Features:** Very hard and tough.
SCHIST – METAMORPHIC ROCK	**Color:** Gray, Silvery or Brown **Original Rock Type:** Clayey rocks with some calcite content such as siltstone **Minerals:** *Majors:* Quartz and Mica *Minors:* many **Texture:** Typically fine-grained but can have medium to large mineral crystals included **Locations:** Very common all over the world **Uses:** Sometimes used as gravel but not often used in building materials. **Features:** Fine grains of mica give the rock a silky and shiny appearance. If broken, schist will break into wavy surfaces.
SLATE – METAMORPHIC ROCK	**Color:** Gray, Blue-Gray, Green, Red or Brown **Original Rock Type:** Shale **Minerals:** *Majors:* Quartz, Feldspar, Carbonates (such as calcite), Chlorite and Micas *Minors:* various **Texture:** Fine-grained **Locations:** France, Finland, United States, England **Uses:** Roof and Flooring material, Blackboards **Features:** Can be broken into sheets. Harder than shale.
TOURMALINE SCHIST – METAMORPHIC ROCK	**Color:** Gray, Silvery or Brown **Original Rock Type:** Siltstone and other clay rocks **Minerals:** *Majors:* Quartz and Mica *Minors:* tourmaline, many others **Texture:** Typically fine-grained but can have medium to large tourmaline crys-tals included. **Locations:** Schist is very common all over the world **Uses:** Sometimes used as gravel but not often used in building materials. **Features:** Fine grains of mica give the rock a silky and shiny appearance. If broken, schist will break into wavy surfaces. Tourmaline schist is a variety of schist that has a prominent amount of tourmaline crystals.

Mineral and Rock Image Gallery

Minerals

Agate Geode	Amethyst	Apatite	Aragonite	Augite
Azurite	Barite	Beryl	Biotite Mica	Calcite
Chalcedony	Citrine	Corundum	Dolomite	Epidote
Fluorite	Galena	Garnet	Gypsum	Halite
Hematite	Hornblende	Iceland Spar Calcite	Kyanite	Lepidolite Mica

Limonite   Magnetite   Malachite   Microcline   Milky Quartz

Feldspar

Muscovite   Olivine   Opal   Pyrite   Quartz

Mica

Jasper   Rhodonite   Serpentine   Sodalite   Staurolite

Sulfur   Talc   Tourmaline   Ulexite

Igneous Rocks

Andesite

Anorthosite

Basalt

Carbonatite

Diorite

Gabbro

Granite

Monzonite

Obsidian

Pegmatite

Peridotite

Pumice

Rhyolite

Scoria

Snowflake

Obsidian

Syenite

Trachyte

Volcanic Ash

Volcanic

Breccia

Sedimentary Rocks

Arkose

Bituminous
Coal

Chert

Conglomerate

Coquina

Fossiliferous
Limestone

Lignite Coal

Limestone

Loess

Oolitic
Limestone

Sandstone

Sedimentary
Breccia

Shale

Siltstone

Metamorphic Rocks

Amphibolite

Anthracite

Coal

Garnet Schist

Granitoid

Gneiss

Gneiss

Hornfels

Marble

Phyllite

Quartzite

Schist

Slate

Tourmaline

Schist

Index

ABOUT THE AUTHOR

Tracy DJ Barnhart is a Professional Geologist and the owner of Mini Me Geology / Giverny, Inc. Mini Me Geology specializes in the development of rock and mineral kits and supplementary teaching aids, eBooks and print books for geology education. A graduate of Furman University and the University of South Carolina, Mrs. Barnhart holds a BS and MS in geology specializing in hydrogeology.

In her free time, Tracy writes a book series, The Crystal Cave Adventures, for elementary and middle school kids who love a little science and science fiction with their adventures. You can find out more about the series at www.CrystalCaveAdventures.com.